COUNTRY PARSON

By

JAMES INSIGHT

FREDERICK FELL, INC.
NEW YORK

First American Publication 1964
By Frederick Fell, Inc., Publishers
386 Park Ave., South, New York 16, N. Y.

Library of Congress Catalog No. 63-23063

COUNTRY PARSON

★ I ★

WE remembered it as soon as we saw it, of course, and the memory winged us back across six years of married life and two small children. The village of St. Hilda's . . .

"Honeymoon Village!"

Perhaps we both said it in unison, or one of us said it and the other only thought it. Anyway, Margaret and I exchanged wary glances and must have trapped expressions of guilt on each other's face. Our discomfort dissolved into peals of laughter. How *could* we have forgotten?

"Well," said Margaret finally, "we both knew we'd heard the name somewhere before. It did, at least, ring a bell."

"But not the church bell," I admitted ruefully.

Our honeymoon visit to St. Hilda's had, it's true, been fleeting. Nevertheless, there was the uneasy feeling that every instant of that blissful period should have remained crystal clear. Six years is not such a very long time. It all came back to us now.

We had been married in the little parish church where Margaret's father conducted the services, in the presence of three coachloads of my own parishioners from St. Silas's. David had been the best man, complete with unruly red beard, flowing cloak and gold-headed cane. Theatrical in appearance, he had been the most impressive figure among those present. Which, I had reflected at the time, was rather hard on the poor bride. However, to make up for this, he had solved the problem of our honeymoon. We'd made no definite plans other than to wander quietly round the West Country, so he'd insisted with his usual charm that we borrow his gleaming sports car and drive off into the unknown. Put that way, the venture had undeniable romantic appeal. Any ideas of my own would have been more prosaic. Just the same, I'd felt obliged to protest a little—knowing, perhaps, that any objections would be swept aside. David had prophesied my marriage and now, even if he wasn't actually coming along, he intended to make sure of the honeymoon.

Accordingly, Margaret and I had driven grandly but noisily away after the reception, David having adorned the back of his superb roadster with an assortment of tin cans, old boots and a horseshoe.

It had all turned out as exciting as David had made it sound—motoring through the West Country, stopping where we would. And it was thus, on the Saturday after our wedding, that we had found ourselves in the vicinity of St. Hilda's.

The village lies in the form of a cross, with the church standing at the rise in the hill where the two beams would normally intersect. Because of its commanding position overlooking the countryside, visitors go into raptures; there is a river, low thatched houses, colourful gardens. Seeing it through the eyes of newlyweds, we had been enraptured. It was Honeymoon Village.

We had stayed just outside the village in a hotel that was approached by a long drive; one of those places inhabited by extremely old people who seem without desire other than to sit about in leathern armchairs. When Margaret and I returned from a walk they would all wake up with a great start and ask what the weather was like. There seemed little likelihood that they would ever find out except by hearsay.

On our first walk we had discovered the church. It was in the village square, set back from the main street. In the main street itself there was an old drinking trough, a number of shops, a pub —encouragingly known as The Cheerful Smile—and next to it a restaurant to which we had gone for morning coffee.

At one end of the village, on a piece of wasteland, someone with a mercenary mind had built a wishing well. Margaret and I held hands and looked into the lily-strewn water to the carpet of coins below, now enriched by some of our own. But our wishes had remained unspoken. Margaret had insisted that it would be unlucky to tell. We were behaving exactly like a couple of honeymooners.

The following morning being Sunday, and obeying the prayer book rubric which says "it is convenient that the new married persons should receive Holy Communion at the time of their marriage or at the first opportunity after", we had gone to the church.

The vicar was one of those hearty God-bless-you-and-do-come-again types. He was standing in the porch shaking hands with members of his congregation as we came out. Catching sight of my dog-collar, he had drawn us aside and held us in conversation. Our enthusiasm for the unusual beauty of St. Hilda's had delighted him and, as we had taken our leave, he had called after us, "God bless you . . ." and then, "Do come again!" It might just have been force of habit, but we'd had a feeling he'd meant it.

The next day, after an early breakfast, we had proceeded on our aimless way, and by lunch time Honeymoon Village had been left far behind. It had been a pleasant interlude but, if anyone had asked, we'd have said that there was small possibility of our ever taking advantage of the vicar's invitation.

Because life is like that, however, we *had* come again. There was nothing spectacular or dramatic about the return visit. We were looking St. Hilda's over—but not in search of lost memories. It was the future with which we were concerned. Was this to be our new home?

Our six years of marriage had been neither unfruitful nor uneventful. The children of a vicar are as much a handful as anyone else's and, apart from the routine task of bringing them up, Margaret had to cope with people constantly calling plus the work I had to do on half a dozen different committees. As if that were not enough, she also helped in a variety of parochial problems. She's never been one to spare herself and, as a result, her health began to suffer. She lost weight and seemed always to be tired. The vicarage itself probably had more to do with this than any other single factor. It was damp, cold and vast. The doctor, after he had given Margaret a thorough examination, did not pull his punches. She was in need of clean fresh air, he said, and as much rest as possible. If she did not get them he would not be responsible for the consequences. "Get her as far away from London as you can," he told me gravely, "and don't let her get involved in a lot of parochial duties." In the face of this ultimatum the only thing I could do was to call on the bishop and ask him for another living.

The bishop lived in a few rooms tucked away in a great palace, the rest of the building being given over to those diocesan offices and organisations which spring up like mushrooms and have to be kept going in order to justify their existence. Nervously I watched the great man push tobacco into his pipe with the end of a pen. Yet I wasn't really scared of him, because behind his gaunt and hollow face were eyes that appeared to be enjoying some private joke.

"It's a thousand pities that a good man like you, Insight, should have to go and bury himself in the country. What does the doctor say in his report?"

"He says, my lord, that Margaret must have more rest, much less work, and better air."

"Country parishes are not the sinecures some people think," he replied. "They can be pretty strenuous. You realise that?" He crossed his legs and sighed. "It's always the way. As soon as a man gets the hang of his parish, he has to go off for some reason or another and we have to begin all over again. However, I suppose it can't be helped."

Something about the expression on my face must have shown him I was hurt because he reached out a hand towards me and said, "I don't quite mean that. We can find you another parish. What we cannot do is find you a new wife. I'll let you know as soon as I hear anything." He was a kind and godly man, and in all my years at St. Silas's I had never known him refuse his help or advice when appealed to. I said good-bye and took my leave, feeling slightly more cheerful than when I'd arrived. At least the bishop realised that there was nothing flippant about my request and that it was because of Margaret.

The palace drive joined a path that ran alongside a private park, leading at last to the drabness of London streets, and the contrasting atmosphere of the green stretches seemed in keeping with the purpose of my visit.

Back at the vicarage, I told Margaret all about the interview
with the bishop and my feeling that everything would be all
right.

"I'm sure it will," she agreed. "But where do you think we
might end up?"

"Well . . ." I said. "It could be anywhere, I suppose."

"Mmm." Her eyes appeared to be seeing far-away places. Then
with a touch of girlishness that had been absent from her recently,
she took one of the children's books from the shelf and opened
it at a map of the British Isles. Finding a pin, she stood over the
book and said, "Let's see if I can forecast." Closing her eyes, she
circled the page three times and then jabbed. "Well?" she asked,
her eyes still tightly shut.

I looked, and smiled. "I devoutly hope you're wrong."

Without working too accurately to scale, the spot she'd chosen
was about ten miles from the coast—seawards into the North
Sea. Vast, cold—and damp!

In due course we received two offers about which we were
not too thrilled, and then the one from St. Hilda's. So it came
about that we went to explore the land.

Few things are more exciting than going to see a place that
you know may one day become your future home. We left the
children—Robert, aged four, and Susan, two—with grand-
parents and arrived incognito at the village.

The fact that we recognised it at once as Honeymoon Village
gave us the impression that it couldn't have changed very much,
but closer inspection made us wonder. We were, in any event,
looking at everything with different eyes. The church, instead
of being a place to attend a service, was something that could
belong to me if I decided to accept the offer. It was, of course, in
the same square as before, but now an opening held room for
cars to be parked and there was a notice that said something about
bye-laws. Neither of us could recall it having been thus on our
first visit. I thought the porch had somehow mysteriously changed
but realised that that, too, could have been a trick of memory.
The scenes of childhood, for instance, can be kept brightly and
vividly alive in one's mind until, daring to revisit them, they

may be found to be dusty and drab and even totally unfamiliar. And, after all, our memories of St. Hilda's were more general than specific. We had been to many places on that honeymoon tour, staying only a short time at each.

Around the corner from the church we discovered the vicarage. By country standards the house looked workable, the last man having divided it into two and kept the better part for himself. It was locked and empty, but we managed to get some idea of the size of the rooms by shading our eyes and peering in through the windows. Going round to the back, we found a large garden. It fell away, down through daffodil banks, to a stream and a rustic bridge.

"We'd have to be careful with the children and the river," said Margaret.

But I, enchanted by the sight of a swan's white in the distance, knew that this was a risk we should have to take.

The beauty of this parish set upon a hill was that you could gaze out over thatched cottages and the back gardens of higgledy-piggledy houses to a soft vista of green fields, rich earth and tall, beckoning trees. But it was not merely the panorama that impressed me. More important was the sweetness and purity of the air—exhilarating, almost intoxicating. This was the tonic that Margaret required; just, indeed, what the doctor had ordered. After London, it was like heaven.

Travelling home, we had tea in the train. Rocked by the motion of the carriage, we talked and toyed with cakes wrapped in cellophane. But even before any words were spoken, we both knew that we had made up our minds to accept the living.

"I wish we could have seen the inside of the vicarage," Margaret said. "But it seemed all right from the outside, didn't it? I mean, there couldn't be much wrong with it, could there?"

"Well," I replied, cutting into a small yellow cake dotted with raisins, "it certainly couldn't be as bad as where we are at the moment." I was as anxious as she that there should be no snags. "We'll have to make a less informal visit before anything is finalised, so we'll have an opportunity to really look it over when we come again."

Margaret didn't answer for a moment. She seemed to be thinking of something. Then she looked across at me with sparkling
eyes.

"God bless you," she said mischievously, "and *do* come
again . . ."

That phrase, remembered and repeated by Margaret, recurred
in my mind during the chaotic week prior to our departure from
St. Silas's. Together with my own remembrances of St. Hilda's
and all I expected the change to do for Margaret, it proved a
great help. I do not take easily to upheaval. In fact, I feel I'm
only at my best when everything is going placidly and smoothly.
The constant reminder that the move would be very much worth
while provided the steadying influence I needed.

My main problem was to prevent Margaret from doing too
much. When there was so much to do, this was not easy. Certain
things, she felt, needed not only her supervision but also her
active participation. Over the heavy stuff, however, I was
adamant; and it underlined the state of her health that she gave
in with less of a struggle than I'd anticipated.

What staggered me most of all was the unbelievable amount of
packing that needed to be done. As one accumulates a home over
the years, each hard-won article takes its special place and
becomes an integrated whole. Breaking it down again into its
individual parts proved a real eye-opener. I would never have
realised that we had so many possessions.

As more and more things disappeared into packing cases the
vicarage, never very prepossessing, became increasingly gloomy.
It was no place for the children or Margaret, and I wanted to get
them out of there as soon as possible. We had previously decided
that I should look after everything and see the furniture into
our new home three or four days before we were due to leave.
Then I would return to say good-bye to my parishioners and
collect my family. We had toyed with the idea of Margaret
taking the children to her father's and staying with him during
this period, but she'd have had to come back for the farewell
meeting and it would have entailed much travelling back and

forth. This we were spared by a wonderful offer from Colonel Hartley.

The colonel was one of the wealthier members of my community. He was a vigorous, healthy-looking man who was probably a good deal older than he appeared. In his army days he had served in every corner of what was then the British Empire, but his experiences had served to toughen only his exterior. On the spiritual side, he was a man of great sincerity and a vociferous champion of the under-dog. He worked hard for Overseas Missions and was Chairman of the Refugees Aid Committee. At committee meetings he was given to long and fluent speeches, but in conversation his manner was inclined to be abrupt, almost brusque.

He called at the vicarage on the second day of turmoil just when we'd called a halt to all activity while we drank coffee.

"You've picked the best possible moment," I told him, manœuvring him round and between partly filled packing cases. "Have some coffee."

"No thanks," he replied. "Can't stay. Going away, as matter of fact. The wife and I. To Brighton." He stubbed his toe on something and muttered. It sounded like a fruity swear word because he hopped about, shot me a glance, and mumbled, "Beg pardon."

Margaret came in from the kitchen. She had a tray of coffee.

"Jim, I was thinking. Oh! Hullo, Colonel. Sorry I'm not made up yet. I look a fright."

"You look lovely."

"Do have some coffee. I've just made it."

"No, thanks. We're off."

"Off?! Are you going away?"

"To Brighton. Daughter's given birth. Wants us to stay a few days."

The mess of our move suddenly hit him. "You can't stop here. Damned uncomfortable. Have our house."

"You mean? You want us to stop in your house when you're away?"

"That's what I said."

"That—that's awfully kind. It's amazing."

"Not interfering I hope." He was a man embarrassed by doing good. He coughed. "If you'd rather not, just say so."

"But the children," cried Margaret, coming out of a dream, "you know what children are like. Are you sure?"

"Positive. A home's the place for children. We're off at midday."

Once we'd said "Yes" it was like a military campaign. He shot out orders as a machine does bullets. But it worked. Inside an hour Margaret and the children were installed. I had an agonising few moments trying to stop Robert from pushing the buttons on the Colonel's radiogram.

"Let him," said Hartley. "Let him. He can't hurt it."

"It's the turntable I'm scared of."

"Lock that side of it up. Look. Here's the key. But the radio buttons are meant to be pressed. He can't do any harm. Now we're off. 'Bye."

"We're terribly grateful," said Margaret. "We just can't tell you what it means to us."

"Don't try. 'Bye, me dears."

When they had gone Margaret said, "What is it to have money. Jim, look at those pictures."

It was a great relief to have Margaret removed from the chaos of the vicarage, even though the colonel's house was just around the corner. She couldn't leave the youngsters alone in strange surroundings and would undoubtedly have to watch them closely to ensure they did no unnecessary damage to the colonel's furnishings. So I was able to concentrate on the remainder of the packing without having to keep a wary eye on her.

In due course the removal was effected and I went with the furniture to St. Hilda's to supervise the positioning, returning that same evening. Margaret and I had previously paid a second visit to our new parish, this time armed with the keys of the vicarage. We had met no one and had thoroughly enjoyed ourselves exploring the place, deciding the rooms to use and where everything should go. This should have made things easier, but the removal men seemed to have ideas of their own and there was a good deal of confusion and noise. In the midst of this, a tall, well-dressed gentleman suddenly appeared from behind a bookcase which was in the process of moving laboriously across the room between two workmen. Taking in the scene, my visitor made his business as brief as possible. It wasn't easy but over the thumpings and clatterings and the shouting of instructions and counter-instructions, I gathered that he was one of the churchwardens and if I gave him the keys someone would be in to tidy up the vicarage and have a meal ready for the family on the day of our arrival. He had a double-barrelled name which was lost in a thunderous cry of "Not there, fathead, over 'ere!" Then the dining table marched solemnly between us, and when it had passed he was gone—with the keys, fortunately.

All of this I related to Margaret that evening as I stretched wearily in what must have been Colonel Hartley's favourite armchair.

"How nice of him," Margaret said. "What's his name?"

I closed my eyes, vividly re-living the episode.

"Mr. Something-Something," I murmured without much conviction.

The church hall was filling up rapidly, people pressing in through the main doors, so that Margaret and I—dressed in our best—chose one of the side entrances. In front of us an elderly lady said quite loudly to an equally elderly gentleman, "He's done his time. No one will be really sorry."

Trying to take evasive action so as not to embarrass the old couple, we collided with a lady. "I still cannot believe that you are really going" she said tearfully. "How we shall miss you and the sweet children." It rather made up for the unfortunate words we had just overheard.

Masses of flowers were piled upon the platform, and before the pleasantries commenced there were cups of tea and a number of people rose and sang in strong voices. They did the same thing at every social. Whenever it was suggested that they might well be dropped, someone would point out that they might be offended because they'd always done it and it really didn't do any harm.

At last it was time for the good-byes, and Margaret and I stood shyly to one side until asked to take a place either side of the chairman. We had already been pleasantly surprised to discover that this was Colonel Hartley, who had returned from Brighton especially for the occasion. Picking up a little wad of notes, the colonel cleared his throat and embarked on what promised to be quite a long speech.

While he talked, I took a last look at my congregation. Practically all of them were there, many of the names now almost part of my life: Mrs. Fowler, Mr. Mawn, Mr. Light, Miss Carey-Jones, Miss Ginger, Mr. Frock, Mrs. Tronc. I caught sight of my one-time housekeeper, Mrs. Head, with her son Richard, and tried to re-live my earlier carefree bachelor days. It was hard to realise that this was the end, and I was more moved than I would have thought possible.

Colonel Hartley approached his peroration. "There will always be a corner in our hearts for Mr. and Mrs. Insight," he said, one hand resting on his waistcoat, "and when we're in need of a summer holiday we shall know where to go." This raised a laugh, and we smiled nervously.

A small child with an abbreviated skirt and a blue bow in her hair was pushed forward. She bore a large bouquet but seemed uncertain for whom it was intended. As she stood hesitant, a muted female voice hissed instructions. But by now the little girl was reluctant to part with the offering at all. However, after a short struggle, Margaret took the bouquet from her and murmured her appreciation. The child made one last frantic, desperate snatch to get the flowers back before being whisked from the platform, and this put everyone in high good humour.

It was now my turn to reply and, because I had prepared nothing, I had to rely on the inspiration of the moment. Standing up, I cleared my throat to say my last words to these people with whom I had lived and worked for years. The chatter subsided. A tense, uneasy silence took its place. To restore the balance, I thought it would be best to begin my speech with a joke. This in itself was something of a handicap. The sort of jokes that convulse audiences are the ones that clergymen are not supposed to know, let alone tell. But I did know a perfectly innocuous one that would serve to get me started. Pointing to the flowers massed at the edge of the platform, I began with the story of the gangster's funeral in Chicago. The hearse was smothered with wreaths, and as it passed down the street a taxi driver called out to a colleague, "Say, whose is the funeral?" Laconically the other replied, "I guess it belongs to the guy nearest to the flowers." For the dialogue I adopted an exaggerated American accent which, I hoped, might make up for any deficiency in the humour content of the tale. The story was received with a roar of laughter. Gratified, I hurried on: "Yes, ladies and gentlemen, to-day it is we"—with a nod that included Margaret—"who are nearest to the flowers; and, after many years with you all, the time of our departure is at hand."

Something about that phrase sounded scriptural. The brain, alarmed, did a quick probe and flashed the assurance that it was Paul who had said the words and not Christ, so that was all right—but please be more careful in future.

I continued speaking, the mind automatically checking and re-checking all that the lips rushed to say. One has to be so careful about quoting, or even appearing to quote.

"We're sorry to leave you all." *Not strictly true; "very nearly all" would have been more like it.* "It's been a tremendous experience." *That, at least, was true.* "Now, because of my wife's health we go to a new life and work in the country. As the chairman has said, we hope that you will all come and visit us—but not all at the same time!"

Encouraged by the laughter, I went on to talk about my new parish. "My wife and I have been to see it and we both look forward to being as happy there as we have been here with you. Of course, it will be a little strange at first. For years we have lived with supermarkets, traffic jams, crowded tubes, trolley-buses, Todd A-O cinemas, ice-rinks just round the corner. Now we shall probably feel like a couple of missionaries in darkest Africa come to preach to the pagan. But I'm sure that will soon pass. Life in the country is looking up. It's no longer the sort of existence it was even a few years ago. St. Hilda's is a village with piped water, electricity, a bus twice a day, and don't forget the T.V. aerial clamped to the thatched roofs of almost every one of its cottages."

This reference to television as the ultimate in modern culture produced the laugh I had hoped for. I got a little carried away and went on to say that in the country life could be so quiet that without the aid of television people would go quietly mad.

While they were still smiling happily, I thanked them for their friendship and support and called for God's Blessing on them. I sat down. Through a mist I could see the rows of faces. They're wondering, I thought, what's going to happen now. My time at St. Silas was at last over, and my congregation had come to wish me well. For six years we had worked together, not always in agreement, but each of us, I was sure, in the belief that what he was doing was right. Inevitably there had been moments when one or other of us had met as enemies, but tonight it was as friends. I loved them all.

Margaret and I stood at the door, shaking hands. To my surprise, it was those with whom I had crossed swords most frequently who showed the greatest regret at our leaving; pressing our hands fervently before hurrying away. Like death, departure must have a sanctifying grace.

Back in our bedroom at Colonel Hartley's house, we didn't want to go to bed. We drank a glass of milk and talked over the evening. The Hartleys had vanished after the meeting, having assured us that they would be home on the morning of our actual departure. This meant that they had either returned to Brighton or were themselves putting up at a hotel in town for the next few days. That they should have gone to so much trouble to ensure our comfort during these days of upheaval was jolly decent of them.

From a pocket I pulled the presentation cheque, and thought of the pleasant surprise the bank manager was going to have.

"I feel awful about this, Margaret," I said. "It's a marvellous present. We don't deserve it."

She came close and squeezed my arm.

"Nonsense, darling," she said. "You deserve it all right. Think what a help it's going to be moving into the new vicarage. I thought your speech was very good. There wasn't anything in it to which a soul could object."

It was what I wanted to hear but in actual fact she was wrong. There *had* been something in the speech, something so damaging that it would haunt us for the rest of our stay in the country, would indeed never finally be erased.

THERE was a *whoosh* up the drive and David, in his long, scarlet touring car swung to within an inch of the porch, where we were patiently sitting on our luggage. We had taken our leave of the Hartleys earlier when they had returned only to dash away again shortly afterwards, the colonel to a business meeting and his wife on a West End shopping jaunt.

"We can't thank you enough," Margaret had said, laughing. "You've saved my life!"

"Forget it," said the colonel. "Don't try. That's right, Robert, come along, let's push every button in sight, just for the last time, shall we?"

"He's been dying to get at it," I said, "but we've kept him away."

He took Robert's hand and together they played the push-button set as if it were a piano.

"They've come," cried Margaret. "Robert, thank Colonel Hartley." She began to drag him from the radio. "It *is* good of you, Colonel. Be a good boy. Come on. Don't be silly."

"That's it, Robert," said Hartley. "Have one good dig at Radio Luxembourg and call it a day, eh?"

The thick, double-tread tyres of David's car playfully scattered us with gravel, and Robert, wild with excitement, broke away from Margaret and rushed to play with the two spare wheels jutting from the rear of the car.

A girl with blonde, cropped hair occupied the front seat. She was the sort of girl that men regard admiringly and women watch narrowly. Leaning out, she followed Robert's antics with amusement.

David was out of the driver's seat in a flash. Dressed immaculately in a pale grey suit, with dog collar, and a carnation in his buttonhole, he talked rapidly as he reached for our cases.

"Don't panic. There's plenty of time. This is Amanda, Margaret. Don't move Amanda. She's practically a cripple in her new skirt, Jim. Doesn't she look lovely?"

In his usual brisk way he had everything under control. Without really being aware of how it had come about, we were whisked into the car and the children had each been handed a little bag of sweets. Then, before we had time to worry about having everything with us, we were sliding from the Hartley's door with a throaty roar.

Turning the corner into the road we had known so well, Margaret's hand reached for mine. "Look quickly, darling," she said softly as we came abreast of the vicarage. "It was our first married home." She is a great one for sentiment and, though I will never voice it, I love to hear it. We turned our heads to gaze mournfully at the house we'd so heartily disliked.

There was a short period of silence as we each thought our own thoughts, but the mood changed once we were clear of the familiar neighbourhood.

We talked to David as he drove, speaking back into the driving mirror, placing the words midway between him and Amanda. A child on the knee of each of us, we were deferential—as if he were the benefactor and we the suppliants. It is always like that with David. Although a parson like myself, he is all that I would like to be if only I had the courage.

In a traffic block, a shuddering lorry towered high to our right. David shouted above the noise.

"Now that you're going to be far away, I'll see more of you both; like the people who live next to my church but are always late."

Amanda turned towards him with a smile, her cheek like a newly ripe peach.

David continued: "I've an uncle who lives on the outskirts of your village, Jim. A dear old boy whom I shall always remember with gratitude. Pots of money, green lawns, walled gardens and all that—one of the landed gentry; a real nob. Look him up when you get the chance; Charrington-Hawes is his name, but

you'd better not say I sent you. I put up a shocking black when
I was there last."

"Charrington-Hawes." I repeated, my mind flitting back. "I
think I've already met him. It was a double-barrelled name, anyway. One of the churchwardens."

"Great Scott! I never knew he was a pillar of the church."

"Well, if he's the chap I met, he is. A most forthcoming old
boy."

"Oh, he would be. He's one of the best in his correct, county
way. The last time I saw him was at a family tea-party years ago.
I was wearing an Eton suit or something equally appropriate and
I went round wolfing all the food in sight, meringues, eclairs,
trifle, the lot. Inevitably I was sick, not decently and in private,
but explosively all over his drawing-room carpet. He would have
been justified in tut-tutting a bit, but he didn't. Instead he
mopped me up in a most understanding manner, at the same
time tearing a strip off an aunt who had seen fit to criticise my
unseemly conduct. Though I haven't seen him from that day to
this I still feel a glow of affection for him. In view of his ruined
carpet I'm afraid it's too much to hope he feels the same for me.
Oh, well," he sighed resignedly, "we were all young once, I
suppose."

The traffic began to move again and we nosed past the lorry.

At the station, we leaned from our carriage window. Amanda
had been quite content to be left in the car, and we talked the
way you do to a friend when you've got him to yourself. If David
had been wearing a tie, Margaret would have straightened it.

"She's pretty, David," she said.

"Who? Oh! Yes, isn't she? Adorable. I collect beautiful
objects . . . always have."

The train gave a jolt.

"Come and stay with us," I said.

"Bring . . ." began Margaret.

A whistle sounded urgently.

"Don't say it," David begged. "Don't tempt me. Margaret,
you won't be happy until I'm bound hand and foot in

matrimony, will you? Amanda is a child, just a child. The man who marries her must be without jealousy."

The train was moving and he walked forward, talking.

"When I go back to the car now, she'll probably have two or three admirers. For all I know, they may have taken the car to pieces; but you can be sure there is a perfect explanation, and she'll give it to me with those large, lovely, china-blue eyes wide, wide open. It would be suicide to fall in love with Amanda."

We laughed. He had come to the end of the platform and even walked right down to the end of the sloping part. There he stood, waving, until we were out of sight. We turned back to our seats to find that Robert was making up a little bed for Susan.

I said, "I never meet David without feeling that life is, after all, very much worth living."

The nearest station to St. Hilda's—the village and the church bear the same name—is a halt; the kind of place at which express trains, snorting indignantly, pull up just long enough for one's luggage to be flung out.

Weeks ago I had ordered transport, but this was nowhere to be seen. Nervously, I walked in and out of empty offices.

"It's the country," said Margaret, getting a firm grip on Robert and Susan. "You'll have to get used to it, Jim. Just take it easy. Something will turn up."

After what seemed an eternity, something did. It was an old man leading a horse which, in turn, pulled a flat cart held together by iron bands and half filled with what looked like old oil drums. The day was glorious, and with the sun beating down we put the baggage on board, settled the children beside it and walked along behind.

More than a mile had been covered when the old man left his horse's head and came to the rear of the cart saying, "You'm our new missionary?"

"Well," I said cheerfully, "I suppose you could look on it like that."

"Why be you going to bother with the likes of us?" This was in a rather vicious, almost sarcastic tone, as if it contained some hidden meaning. He didn't wait for an answer, but turned abruptly and resumed his former position.

Margaret and I looked at each other blankly. She opened her mouth to speak, but I beat her to it. "I know—it's the country, and I'll have to get used to it."

The walk seemed interminable, and the few people we passed gazed curiously at us as though they didn't much care for the sight. But the heat was intense and this may have been a mirage, like the one that danced ahead at the tip of the hill.

I mopped my brow. "I wonder if that Charrington-Hawes chappy was as good as his word."

"Which word?" asked Margaret.

"The one about seeing that somebody would be there to have a meal ready for us."

"Just a cup of tea would be nice." There was a note of longing in Margaret's voice and I glanced at her with some misgiving. She was supposed to be resting, and here we were walking, slowly but endlessly, in the blazing sunshine.

When we reached the vicarage the front door was open and the hallway looked cool and inviting, so we wasted no time in disembarking the children and the luggage. As soon as we had done so, the cart trundled away, the old man neither speaking a word nor waiting for the tip I was about to give him.

A lady in a grey costume came from a door at the end of the hall as we crossed the threshold.

"Good," she said. "It's you. Just as I planned. I thought you'd be arriving about now and would feel like a cup of tea. It's all ready in the kitchen."

We followed her thankfully.

Pulling out chairs from the table, she went on talking. "I'm not only one of your parishioners, you know, I'm also a neighbour. My cottage is quite near. I told Mr. Charrington-Hawes I'd be only too pleased." She guided us to our places. "My name is Charmian. Some French connection there. Quite a few people round here have similar names, you know. Names like Le Sœuf and Chambre." She pronounced the words as if she loved them, adopting a French accent; and as she talked she took Susan from Margaret's arms, sat her down and gave her a lump of sugar from the bowl on the table. Then she began to pour the tea.

Margaret's face was dead white from fatigue, and across the children's was a grey film of dust from the journey. The sight of the table revived us all: rich slices of red ham, lettuce with drops of water gleaming upon the leaves, beetroot, a bowl full of cream, jelly and trifles.

I was asked to say grace.

When we opened our eyes, Robert—for no apparent reason— burst into tears. Mrs. Charmian leant across and, doing it all with one hand, tucked a napkin beneath his chin, placed jelly in a little dish before him, and poured cream liberally all over it. "Tired— very, *very* tired," she said softly to us; then to him, briskly, "I've got a surprise for you, Robert. There's a swan's nest not far away and I'm going to take you to see it. Would you like that?"

Robert gulped, searching for his spoon. "Yes," he said.

Something in his meek agreement, instead of the fierce temper we knew so well, stabbed my heart, reminding me of actions in others that never failed to move me deeply: a child who, in a quarrel, removes her spectacles to wipe tears away; a cat offering its paw with a thorn sticking out; a mother, at midnight, with the ironing piled like a pyramid before her.

"Margaret," I said, "you ought to get to bed early. I'll do the washing up."

"Everything is ready," said Mrs. Charmian. "The beds are made and I've put hot bottles in to air them." She looked at me. "Vicar, why not go and have a look at your church and the village? I'm sure you're longing to. Leave the family to me. I expect we will have a look at the garden and then start getting everyone tucked up." She hugged Susan. "With picture books, if they can't drop off to sleep quickly."

"Swan's nest," said Robert, urgently.

The church was small, rather like a large drawing room. A dozen people would look quite a large congregation and speaking would be no strain at all. There was a dusty, dismal air about the place.

I walked into the vestry. It was in need of a good tidying out. Backless prayer books, collection of grim-looking gloves, umbrellas and spectacle cases were all scooped together and stuck in an alcove beneath a lopsided cross.

Pulling out a chair, I sat at the table, opened the service book and ran a finger along the columns that contained communicant numbers ... 4, 6, 8, 3—20! Whatever had occurred there? After London, the figures appeared terribly small.

"Arr ... arrr ..."

It was a deep country voice and it nearly made me jump out of my skin. Closing the book, I turned to face its owner.

"Hu-hullo," I began, not too brightly. "I'm the vicar."

"Thought you were Mr. Jones. Either it were him, I said to myself, or poor Danny." He was the verger, wearing a black, flapping gown which gave him a fore-shortened look.

"Isn't Mr. Jones the People's Warden?" I asked.

His face brightened. "Finest gentleman living. I take my orders from him."

"Yes ..."

"Best friend this church ever had. 'Fred,' he says, 'Fred Quimbolt, if there's anything ever you want then ask me.' The things he done for this church is past all compre——is past all——it just beats everything."

"It's a lovely building, Mr. Quimbolt," I ventured. "I want to see it shining with polish and paint and as great a showplace as the village."

"I'll need to speak to Mr. Jones about that. No good talking to Mr. Charrington-Hawes ..."

I stood up. "We could begin with this vestry. What about a thorough clear-out? Get rid of all these old missionary boxes and out-of-date papers. Throw the lot away. Give the place a good scrub, Quimbolt."

He shook his head, saying he would not like to rush at an important thing like that: water might get down between the boards and start rot. He'd need to have a long chat with his wife, who did any scrubbing that needed doing. He'd tell me what, though—he would ask Mr. Jones what he thought about it all.

Before I left him, he said, "Aren't you going to call me Fred? Everyone in the village calls me Fred."

Walking down the village street, the inflection of his voice was still with me. Nothing would be nicer than to start off on Christian-name terms at once, but experience had shown that it didn't always pay. One never knew how soon a difference of opinion might crop up and, as far as I was concerned, it would be easier to argue with Mr. Quimbolt than with Fred.

On either side of the street were thatched cottages with carefully tended miniature gardens. In many instances television masts stood parallel with chimneys. It was nice to know that some of the homes had the means of relieving the boredom of long winter evenings, still many months ahead. We had chosen the best time of the year to make our move. The village of St. Hilda's had, on this particular evening, the look of a girl still in the freshness of youth. Looking around me, I knew there were many people who would willingly have changed places with me. I had a house, a job, and an income—small, of course, by modern standards— and all in the country, in glorious surroundings. As with the most perfect of roses, however, one couldn't help but anticipate a tiny thorn. This was a stolid, tight little community, so compact that if anything should happen to make my parishioners annoyed with me there would be precious little I could do to avoid their wrath. Here there were no thronging masses of people and cafés and long streets to preserve anonymity.

In one of the houses to my right a curtain moved. The occupant, peering out, caught sight of me and too obviously took to looking at nothing. These people were aware all right that the new vicar of St. Hilda's had arrived.

"Please, Lord," I prayed, turning into the main shop in the village, "let me please these people in doing Thy work. Don't let me do anything to upset them as I have sometimes foolishly upset my parishioners in the past."

There were only three or four people in Bradley's. I was glad of this because it gave me a chance to look round the shop. As one might expect from a village store it seemed to have every-thing, with a captivating mixture of old and new: sacks of dog biscuits and corn, modern bacon cutters and cash registers, old-fashioned paraffin stoves. There were even things up aloft, hang-ing politely from the ceiling as if they were doing their best not to be in the way.

Behind the counter, a woman was slowly wrapping a pound of butter. As she did so, she listened, head on one side, to the customer's chatter. This was all about an undisciplined family known as the Raffertys who, it seemed, were up to their tricks again.

At long last, the customer took her butter and other purchases and turned from the counter. "Good evening, all," she said as she made her way to the door. Pausing in the entrance, she called, "You won't forget, will you, Mrs. Bradley?" before bustling out.

Mrs. Bradley smiled at me. "It's that *Hands that wash dishes can be soft as your face* stuff she wants. Like they advertise on the telly. I've got some coming in from London, you know. Would you like me to serve you next? You're such a busy man, you won't be wanting to waste your precious time in here. You *are* the new vicar, aren't you? Of course. Do you know Miss Splinter over there by the dog biscuits who sings in the choir? And old Mr. Jervis next to her?" Taking time only for a very snatched breath, my interrogator suddenly screamed: "And how's that back of yours, Mr. Jervis? And—how—is—that—back —of—yours—— It's no good, he can't hear a word. *Come over here . . .*"

She had him leaning across the counter while she shouted the same thing, word for word, into his gnarled ear. Everyone looked on and smiled and then looked at me to see if I was smiling.

"Not in a hurry, are you, Vicar?"

"Oh, no—no."

"Dear old man, isn't he?"

"Marvellous."

"I'll serve him now, while I've got him here. He never knows what he's doing. His wife has to undress him and put him to bed, you know." Then she screamed out again, "You're my sweetheart, aren't you, Mr. Jervis!"

I managed to get through the next quarter of an hour by refusing to glance at my watch and reminding myself that this was the country and I'd have to get used to it. Then, at last, I ordered the daily newspapers and bought a bottle of ink and some envelopes. Mrs. Bradley prattled on as she elaborately wrapped these items.

"I *am* looking forward to meeting your wife, Vicar, I really am. It'll be a pleasure to get her orders. I spend most of Sunday doing the books you know. It's the only time I get; but I'll certainly come to church whenever I possibly can. There's nothing like a nice church service, I always say. I wish I could go more often. That cereal over there is new, you know. It pops and crackles. The children love it, and I think there's a spaceship in every packet. I've got quite a stock of new things in from London, you can tell your wife."

Under cover of showing me these things, she took every opportunity to look me up and down. It seemed as if she felt she shouldn't like me but was torn between some inexplicable prejudice and the means of her daily bread. I left the shop assuring her that I wouldn't forget to give my wife her very kindest regards.

It was, I felt, about time I returned to the vicarage. Wanting to delay the moment in the perfection of the evening, however, I took a narrow pathway that bit through the village, passing numerous quaint houses that I longed to visit and coming out upon the slopes above.

Here were better-class houses, further removed from each other than those I had already seen. At the door of one of them a woman with short cropped hair and spectacles sat with a saucepan beside her. She was peeling potatoes, dropping the skins into a newspaper that was spread open upon her lap. Looking up, she spotted me, gave me a quick all-embracing look and called out, "Come in and have a chat."

In order to do so, I had to tackle the gate. It was the kind you have to lift bodily, carry with you for a while and then set back into position. This done, I was free to join her.

Sitting myself beside her on the doorstep, I said, "I'm the new vicar. I've just arrived."

"I know. Mrs. Charmian was in the vicarage to welcome you. What do you think of her?"

"I—well——" I stumbled, confused.

She smiled. "I shouldn't have asked you. I like her very much."

"So do I."

"But you are quite right not to gossip." She carried on with her task. "Let me give you some advice. You'll never stop gossip in a village. The best thing is to use it for good. I've had to hammer this thing out for myself. Years ago—it doesn't matter now what the reason for it was—I became the target for everyone's tongue and I had to make up my mind what I was going to do. One day, perhaps, I may tell you what it was all about."

"You don't believe, then, in keeping things to yourself?"

"I do," she replied, "but others don't. What happens now is that I get to know everything and use the knowledge for the best."

"How do you know what happens?" I couldn't help asking.

"People tell me. As they pass the gate, they drop in or call across. For instance, I know that you had ham for tea. I know your children's ages and names. I know why—at least, I *think* I know why you are out on your own to-night."

The pieces of potato plopped softly into the saucepan by her foot. "I do these the day before," she volunteered, "so that there's less work the next day." Then, without looking up, "I know that you've already had a set-to with Fred Quimbolt, the verger."

I gaped at her, aghast. "Of course I haven't!"

She bowed her head and said quite equably, "I interpret what I hear."

"The church is filthy."

"I know that, and I'm delighted if you're going to do something about having it cleaned up. Fred's completely in Farmer Jones's pocket."

"I thought that he . . ." I let my voice trail off. Whatever was I about to say?

She laughed. "In time you'll come to trust me—and talk to me."

"In my job," I said, "I can't do that."

"Not about intimate things concerning individuals," she went on with quiet certainty, "but about the over-all politics of the village. And you will never divorce the church from this. As soon as the people begin to hurt you, you'll come to me for advice. You see."

I answered her with equal certainty. "Why should people want to hurt me? I certainly don't intend to hurt them. I want to do my work and take life quietly. I've had enough excitements in the last parish. Now I just want to try to lead myself, my family and my people a little closer to God."

She didn't say anything, finishing the last potato—a little brute of a thing, all knobs and eyes—and dropping it with a sigh into the water. When she did speak, it seemed that our discussion had been abandoned. "Come and see the view from the back garden," she said.

Rising, she led the way into the house, a short, masculine figure with the cropped hair, leather coat and thick shoes; one of those solid, dependable people, incapable of a mean action.

"Don't look at the mess," she said. "It's the dogs—here, Budsy, Scamper." Then, as they came leaping, tails wagging excitedly, "There, boy, down. Down, *down*, blast you. That's better. Shake hands with your new vicar." But as neither dog seemed prepared to go that far, she shooed them off and said, "You'll have to come into the garden if you want to see more order."

At the back there was a glorious view, away to what she told me was Farmer Jones's farm; and beyond, the large, ornate, behind-walls house of Charrington-Hawes.

"If they were eggs," she said, half to herself, "the world would grade him above t'other; but I wouldn't." She flashed me a lively look from beneath her thick eyebrows. "It isn't fair, is it? I'm longing to talk, but I mustn't until you are ready for it."

We went back into the house and she brewed chocolate, hunt-

ing for the cups, biscuits and sugar from among the parapher-
nalia of the kitchen. I knew I should be hurrying back to
Margaret, for more than an hour had passed since I left the
vicarage. As we sipped our hot chocolate, I said: "The villagers
are suspicious of strangers, aren't they? How long shall I have
to live here before I'm accepted and not regarded as a foreigner?"
I told her of the carter's peculiar manner on the way from the
station, the curious looks from people we'd passed, and the
strange sense of antipathy I had experienced in Bradley's shop.

When I'd had my say, there was a long silence. With anyone
else it might have bothered me. But sitting there, with our empty
cups and the plate of uneaten biscuits before us, there was something companionable about it. So that, when she finally spoke,
I was completely unprepared for the nature of her reply.

"Suppose I told you that you have already upset the village?"
I could scarcely credit my ears. "But I've only just arrived."

"You'd better hear it from me," she said. "And because I like
you and believe we shall be friends whatever happens, I'm glad
it has turned out like this and I can break the news." She
hurried from the room.

What on earth was all this about? What could I have possibly
done? My mind raced back to the moment of our arrival at the
station and tried to recall every move, every word since. There
was nothing—except my conversation with Mr. Quimbolt about
the state of the church. But would that be enough to upset a
whole village? Surely not. Then what? Nothing ... I hadn't had
time to do anything.

She came back into the room with the newspaper she'd had
on her lap, the peelings still on it. Shaking them into a bucket
beneath the sink, she folded the paper and, marking the place
with a thick thumbnail, she folded the paper and handed it to
me.

Despite my bewildered state, I noticed the name "Mrs. Pankhurst" pencilled across the top corner of the paper—presumably
by the newsagent—and wondered if this was her name and if
she was in any way related to the famous suffragette.

The heading she had indicated was in large enough type to

catch the eye. It read: "Vicar Likens New Parishioners to Pagans." The column beneath this began: "The Rev. James Insight, to be inducted next week to the living of St. Hilda's, regards his new parishioners from a missionary's angle. Speaking at a farewell meeting in his old parish in London, he said . . ."

In a cold sweat, I read the substance of my farewell speech three days ago.

★ 3 ★

How a London daily newspaper came to give so much space to
the farewell meeting at St. Silas's is one of those mysteries that
will remain, I suppose, for ever unexplained. They must have
been desperately short of news that day. It's true that I've had a
couple of books published and that they've sold quite well, but
I haven't yet been hailed as another Hemingway or an embryo
Somerset Maugham. Nobody's even asked me for my autograph.
So it's hardly likely that the London dailies would have reporters
dogging my footsteps and rushing into print with my every
spoken word. The only thing I can think of is that some cub
reporter happened to be present, wrote the meeting up, sub-
mitted it and, happily for him, happened to catch the paper
between murders. Or maybe the piece was only printed in the
West Country editions as being of topical interest. Whatever the
reason, as far as I was concerned it was a stroke of infernal bad
luck. My hope of finding peace in the country had been shattered
before I'd even arrived.

Not that the newspaper had been deliberately unfair. My words
hadn't been twisted. All that had happened was that emphasis
had been placed on those unguarded words uttered in fun, so
that they now carried a real sting in their tail. Reading the
account, there was a difference—the vast, insurmountable difference between the spoken and the printed word. The speaker,
with the aid of tone, cadence and inflection, has the opportunity
of guiding his audience to a complete understanding of what
is in his mind. The printed word, on the other hand, is blank
and cold—open to whatever interpretation the reader cares to
give it. And in print, the part of my speech referring to my new
parishioners could at best be termed unfortunate. From that
moment on, I was aware of it; and so were others. The result
was that I found myself looking for undercurrents of resentment
in everyone with whom I found myself in conversation.

Even the rural dean was not exempt. We met him, and numerous other people, at the social in the church hall which followed my institution. A large, heavy man, with a face that struck me as being a cross between that of the late President Roosevelt and a sheep, he limped across and offered me, literally, two fingers.

"Sorry I haven't more, Insight," he apologised lightly. "I keep having to go into hospital so that they can take away some further portion of my anatomy."

"I'm sorry, sir," I said rather inadequately.

"Yes, well ... Delighted to have you in the Deanery. And you, Mrs. Insight. You'll both help to lower the average age." He paused for a moment and my mind telegraphed *Now!* So I was not really surprised when he continued with: "By the way —this newspaper report ... Not unduly worried, are you?"

"I can't get it out of my head, sir," I admitted.

"Try to forget it. It wasn't the wisest of remarks to make, my boy, but it's easy to see how it happened. If it had happened in a London parish nobody would have cared a tinker's cuss, but in the country it's different. In the country people are inclined to believe implicitly in what they read in the newspapers. They are inclined to jump to conclusions and leave out several rather important intermediary stages."

"I'll remember, sir," I said, grateful for his understanding.

"Yes. Don't let it spoil these early months when you're settling in and getting to know people. It doesn't do to become too sensitive. Copy the rhinoceros, eh?" He paused again briefly. "I must be off. Whenever I come over, I renew contacts with one or two rather good friends I've made in your parish. Do you know a Major Icely?"

"I think he's on the P.C.C.," I said, recalling the name.

"Sure to be. I'll be interested to hear how you two get on. And a Mrs. Pankhurst?"

"I've met her."

"Yes. Well ..." He tapped one of my legs with his stick as a salutation and stumped away.

Watching him, deep in conversation with a soldierly looking

man by the door, the thought came to me that Mrs. Pankhurst could have rung him up and told him all about my predicament. It made no difference, anyway.

Charrington-Hawes turned out to be an abrupt sort of man and I summed him up as one of the old-school, accustomed to having his own way. Margaret stood smiling reflectively at him, no doubt recalling the tea-party scene David had painted so graphically. After the introductions, he addressed himself exclusively to me. He would like, he assured me, to foot the bill for any debts the church might incur and also—provided I had no objection—he would like to continue to pay for the children's annual treat. The thanks were scarcely dry upon my lips when he said, "Sorry about this newspaper report."

"So am I," I replied.

"One sees it was intended as a joke, of course, but not a very clever one in the circumstances."

"Don't I know it!" I said. "I'm spending all my time apologising."

"Oh well, as long as it doesn't happen again."

"It won't . . ."

"As your warden, I am sure we shall get on together. If I object to anything, I shall say so quite candidly."

"I like that sort of person," I said. "You know where you are with each other then." Saying the words, I thought how uncomplicated it would be if relationships between people really were like that.

Although others were waiting to talk to us, he stayed some time, insisting on fixing the date of the next P.C.C. and making sure that I wrote down on a piece of paper—which I knew I would lose—points that he wished raised. He seemed to attach great importance to these points although, on the face of it, their urgency escaped me. However, not wishing to risk another reprimand, I earnestly recorded them. Before he walked away, he said that we must bring the family to see him at his home. It was an invitation, but it had the ring of a command.

Farmer Jones was very friendly. With trousers in at the knee, maroon waistcoat and knobbly stick, he looked exactly the popular conception of a farmer. He seemed to be a great one for the ladies, eyeing them—Margaret included—with the sort of expert discrimination that one might have expected him to reserve for a cattle show. He was well acquainted with most of the women present and introduced many of them to us. His wife was busy with the teas, and probably glad of it. When we did get around to her, she seemed very shy and nervous, constantly looking at her husband to see if she had said the right thing.

I had reached the point now where I was mentally deciding at exactly which moment each person I met would mention the newspaper report. But with Farmer Jones I was wrong. He didn't mention it at all, and for that I was grateful. Not only did it give me a respite from apologies but it fostered the hope that in time the wretched business would die down and I would be free from the fear of my people.

Fortunately there were to be no speeches, since everyone knew who I was and had just seen me installed. It was fit and proper, however, that tea and sandwiches should be served as the bishop was with us. The great man shook us each by the hand and wished us well, but said very little else. In fact, he seemed relieved when his archdeacon hurried across the hall to tell him that his car was waiting.

The bishop's departure meant that this opening ordeal was nearly over. Other people began to leave and we knew that we would soon be able to go home and relieve Mrs. Charmian, who was looking after the children.

I was mentioning this to Margaret when a voice said, "You both look tired out."

It was the soldierly looking man to whom the Rural Dean had been talking. He put out a hand to each of us in a fatherly manner, though he was not old.

"My card, Vicar," he said, proffering it. "And when you have a moment, we'll have a chat. But may I suggest that you both get off to bed now?"

I smiled. "Do you think it would be all right?"

"Perfectly. I'll say that I made you. I am your P.C.C. secretary."

We fled—down the path, through the little gate, round the corner and up the drive.

In the vicarage, I glanced at the card. It said *Major Richard Icely, M.C.*, and the address was *The Nook, St. Hilda's.*

On the following morning, the first of a number of people I was to meet in the coming weeks presented himself on the doorstep. He was wearing narrow corded trousers and had a scarf at his neck. The rest of his clothing was unusual—it defied immediate classification.

"Welcome to St. Hilda's," he began, giving a little old-fashioned bow. "My wife and I live in a converted barn three miles outside the village but within the parish."

"Good," I said, "I'd very much like to visit you."

Since he had come to visit me, however, I took him into the study and seated him in a chair facing mine. His clothes, on closer inspection, were hand sewn and in a pale grey material. As soon as we were settled in our chairs, he produced a visiting card and laid it on my knee. Its message was brief: *Samuel H. Saigon, F.R.G.S.*

"We live in stirring times, Vicar," he said, giving the "r"'s a soft burr. "I spend my whole time working for peace."

"Very wise of you."

"I have come this morning to ask your permission to have a large peace service in St. Hilda's."

I opened my mouth to speak, but he held up a hand.

"Don't say anything. We—me and my helpers—will do all the preparatory work. You need do nothing, nothing at all. But we would, of course, be honoured by your presence at our service."

I waited for a moment, just in case, but his hands remained loosely clasped in his lap. This time he did want me to say something. It was not a matter about which I could readily commit myself, and I said cautiously, "I'd really have to make some enquiries."

"Do. Do. Ask anyone in the village. They all know Saigon. I spend my entire time working and writing for peace." He paused, but not long enough for me to make any comment. "These are stirring times. If you really want to work for peace, there can be no reason why you shouldn't support my plan for a peace service."

"Every service we have in church is a peace service."

"Is it? Is it? Look, sir, at the world." He flung out his arm and my eyes followed its direction to the window. Outside, the cloud was low and heavy across the glebe and there was a hint of thunder in the air.

"I'll have to ask the wardens how the people in the village would feel about it, Mr. Saigon; but if they offer no objection I personally think it would be a splendid idea to have a service. Perfectly splendid."

"Thank you, Vicar."

"Mind you," I added incautiously, "I sometimes wonder if merely talking about peace is the best way of achieving it."

"Vicar!" he exclaimed, shocked.

I tried to make him understand what I meant.

"Look, Mr. Saigon, the whole world talks of peace. Conferences go on and on and on. So does the arms race. And every weapon more hideous than the last. It's just a mockery. It's action we want more than words."

"But..." He searched for words. "We must learn to *trust* our fellow men. If you don't have faith..."

"Man is human. He's neither all good nor all bad," I said. "The battle goes on inside him. St. Paul told us that, 'the good that I would I do not: but the evil which I would not, that I do'. And even when God gives a man a new heart the battle still rages. I just can't accept people merely on the grounds of what they say. I try to, but just as you get used to the idea, something happens to upset the apple-cart. I see human beings as creatures who if they are thwarted or crossed or have the opportunity will stop at nothing to get their own way; will lie and cheat and hate and murder. Sometimes I get so that I wouldn't trust one living creature."

"No?"

"I wouldn't even trust myself," I said, getting up, "not myself nor even you, professed man of peace that you undoubtedly are."

"What a confession, Vicar!" He was genuinely shocked. "However," he went on, "I'm glad we can have the service."

"I haven't promised."

"There won't be any objection. In this village I have organised meetings, sales of work, outings—all in the cause of peace. The village is thoroughly peace minded. Not pagan minded, Vicar. Decidedly not pagan minded."

It was like a blow below the belt, I thought at first; but he was smiling affably, unaware of the sting his words carried. Obviously they'd been said in innocence. When would I be free from such doubts?

There seemed no more to be said at the moment, and I escorted him from the study. At the front door, Margaret was settling Susan for a sleep on the porch.

"Your dear wife?" Mr. Saigon asked. He took her hand. "Your dear husband is going to be a great blessing to this parish and we have just had a most helpful time together."

"I'm so glad," said Margaret.

Mr. Saigon took my arm, leading me away down the drive, talking as we went. "I'll be in again very soon. I shall bring literature, seating plans, proposals. You need have no worries at all. But tell me, Vicar——" He looked at me oddly. "Where do you get your, shall we say—unusual, views?"

It is rarely that one can give the kind of reply that one would like to give on the spur of the moment. Usually it comes to mind hours later when it is no longer of any use. This time, however, it was easy. Without having to go through any involved thought processes, I said simply, "From the Bible."

Nevertheless, it was he who had the last word.

"Why—why, Vicar—that's just where I get mine!"

Bill Tomlinson and the *County Times* arrived within an hour or so of each other on Friday morning. The newspaper came first, at about eleven o'clock. I heard a noise at the front door and rushed out in time to stop the delivery boy from shredding a thick wad of newsprint through the letter box.

Eager to see how the local news was presented, I took the paper into the study. Published in the town, five miles away, it seemed much given to advertising second-hand cars, displays of ladies' corsets, and columns of reports about funerals.

I've never known a paper to have such a penchant for funerals. There wasn't a detail that passed unnoticed. Everyone who attended the service was mentioned by name and anyone unable to be present was written down as being represented by a friend, like royalty. The inscriptions on the wreaths were set out in full, no matter how harrowing—"To Mum, who never complained," or "Alf, you always had a smile, from Jos, Jim and Little Titch." It was exactly the sort of material that would guarantee the paper's circulation, since most people enjoy seeing their name in print, and it may have accounted for the large numbers of people present who were neither relatives nor friends of the deceased.

It was interesting, therefore, to meet Bill Tomlinson, for it was he who so meticulously reported these goings-on in the *County Times*. If I'd thought about it at all, I would have imagined him to be a tall, gaunt, cadaverous individual with mournful eyes and a down-drawn mouth. In fact, he was a fair-haired, shy young man who lived with his mother over a fried fish shop.

He must have timed his call to allow me to get acquainted with the paper, which everyone in the village took. Standing awkwardly on the doorstep, he told me that he'd be calling each week for any news items I might have.

"Come in," I said.

"Are you sure, sir? I don't usually get asked in."

"Quite sure," I smiled, showing him into the study. "In London we had to coax bits into the paper instead of having reporters call on us!" Except for one unfortunate occasion, I thought. But if he wasn't going to mention that incident, I certainly wouldn't.

"I make a round of the vicarages every week, sir," he explained. "It's part of my training, like a policeman's beat. We're glad of anything, even if you may not think of it as particularly interesting."

"Of course." I thought for a moment. "Well...it looks as if there's a disused tennis court in the glebe. I was wondering if I could get some of the young people to resurrect it; it would give them something useful to do...I hear there's rowdiness from children in the village and farmers talk about broken hedges, crippled hens, overturned milk churns..."

"Just a minute, sir, please—I can't get it down quickly enough."

The thought crossed my mind that I was treading on dangerous ground again. Those last remarks could easily be turned into more damaging headlines. Too late now. I'd have to trust to his discretion. It wouldn't do any harm, though, to change the subject.

"The verger has been digging in the churchyard and he's unearthed a vault in which he discovered an old book that looked like a diary..."

"That's interesting, sir," he said, writing furiously. "Can I use it?"

"Why not?"

"Have you told the P.C.C.?"

"Not yet; but you'd better have news while it's still 'hot', hadn't you?" There was every possibility that it would have cooled off a little by the time it appeared the following Friday, anyway.

He put down his notebook. "I wish all vicars were as helpful as you, sir."

"I wish all reporters came to church, like you."

He flushed and said, "I like to go to church."

The nervous tension was beginning to leave him and I tried to draw him out about his work for the paper. But his attention had been caught by my bookshelves and, instead, I found myself answering questions about some of my theological volumes. This was not for publication. His interest was personal and genuine.

Struck by it, I said, "You may borrow some of them if you wish."

"Oh, sir!"

"I have duplicates. I had an uncle who was a parson and he gave me a lot. Would you like a whole set of Spurgeon's sermons? And I can let you have a few odd copies of Matthew Henry."

His joy was immense, and finding some string we tied the books neatly together so that he could carry them away on his bicycle. In his happiness, he started to take me into his confidence. It had always been his ambition to become a clergyman; but the death of his father, with the consequent need to support his mother, had prevented him from taking his General Certificate Examination. Now that he was earning more, he had commenced to study again.

When he had gone, I saw that he had forgotten his notebook. Inside the front cover was his name and address and a snapshot of a pretty girl in a gym tunic. Opening the front door to see if he was still within shouting distance, I found him pedalling furiously towards me. He braked as he reached the doorstep but did not dismount.

"I only came back, sir," he panted, "to ask if you would be so good, should you meet my mother when out visiting, not to mention what I said about wanting to be ordained." He gulped and pulled a face. "You see, she wants me to become a great success in Fleet Street."

"In that case," I said, "you'd better take greater care of this."

I handed him his notebook.

After lunch, I went for a stroll. Just outside the village I was stopped in my tracks by the sight of what appeared to be a Swiss chalet plumped down in the middle of the very English countryside. The gate giving access to it bore the information that this was The Nook. As I stood admiring it all, a voice called out: "Come in. Come in, Vicar. Delighted to see you."

Major Icely was astride a tree towards the back of the house and could see me across the hedge. I thanked him and walked through to the foot of his tree.

"I like your house," I called, peering up at him.

"Wait one moment, old boy."

He was dropping the fruit from the branches on to a blanket, so that they fell comfortably and unbruised. Then, in a series of rapid movements, he swung to the ground.

"There," he said, standing beside me, "that tree's finished." He gathered up his booty. "I spend the summer preparing for the winter. These will all be chopped up and bottled."

With brisk energy, he whisked me on a sightseeing tour of the garden. There was a large expanse, every part of which had been utilised. And everything was immaculate—tools labelled, potting sheds prepared, huts cleansed. Creature comforts had not been overlooked, either. The summer-house contained not only a radio set and a telephone extension but also a serviceable-looking teapot. It may have been the sight of this that made him say, "Let's go into the house, Padre. I'm sure you'd like some tea." He led me through a glass parlour adjoining the lawn. "You see? Double windows throughout the house. We'll need them in a few months' time." Then he snapped down on a switch on some electrical contraption and consulted his wrist watch. "In ten minutes, at precisely sixteen hundred hours, Padre, tea will be made, eggs boiled, toast prepared and the wireless turned on. Ten minutes in which to have a wash."

As we went up the stairs to the bathroom, he inspected a thermometer on the wall. "I have twenty-two of these, Padre, spread throughout the house. Not expensive things. I like to know the temperature at any given spot. Never be without thermometers."

The house was as highly organised as the garden. Wherever he took me there was evidence of advance planning—the breakfast things laid in one room, the lunch things in another.

"It's the most marvellous house I've ever visited," I said.

"Thanks . . . but don't let me bore you with it. I'd hate to be a bore."

Upon our return downstairs, everything was as he had prophesied. Tea was ready, with lightly boiled eggs and crisp toast; and music was flooding the room. The timing device had seen to it all.

The music from the radio was so clear that the musicians might well have been in the thick carpeted room with us. It deserved to be listened to, rather than used as a background to conversation.

"Great stuff, isn't it, Padre?" Major Icely went across and turned down the volume before taking a seat. "Hi-fi. You must bring your wife some time and have an evening of records."

Over tea, he told me how he came to be living as he was. His father had left him some money and he had retired from the Army before his time with a reduced pension. The actual business of living, he felt, was exciting enough without the encumbrance of a job. And he found so much to do that the days just weren't long enough. This despite the fact that the house was crammed with labour-saving devices of every description.

Suddenly he switched the conversation to me, asking all about my previous parish and my plans for St. Hilda's. He was not just being polite. One could sense a lively interest behind his questions.

"Settling in can be quite a business," he said, "particularly if people start getting difficult. I could probably save you a lot of worry and trouble by telling you what I know about the people in the village—but you wouldn't think much of me if I did. One has to work these things out for oneself; in a village we tend to get to know each other pretty well, no matter how we hide ourselves."

We went on to talk about the church and its work, checked on a date for the P.C.C., and finally came back to the subject of his house.

"It's all so wonderful," I said, "that one suspects there must be a catch somewhere. But of course——"

"There is," he replied.

"*Is* there?" I was surprised because I really hadn't seen any flaws.

"You're married," he said quietly. "Any children?"

"Yes. Two."

"There you are, then. I'm not married, and therefore all this seems wasted. There's no one to share it with . . ."

Margaret was in the kitchen when I got back to the vicarage. She had on over her dress a blue plastic apron on which was a sugar-cube pattern in the form of a little man cooking.

I told her about Icely's house, saying that he wanted her to see it and that we must buy her a new dress for the occasion. Her face brightened.

"He's not married, Margaret," I said, remembering the tone of his voice when he told me. "If only we could find him a wife his life would be complete."

"Really, darling . . . !" She seemed amused. "He must know everyone in the village, and we hardly know a soul. If he hasn't found someone himself, how much success would we have?" She giggled. "Match-makers Incorporated."

"There must be someone," I said doggedly.

Margaret thought for a moment. "What about Amanda?"

"Amanda?" I looked at her in astonishment. "But Amanda is—well, I mean—David——"

"David can look after himself."

Women have extraordinary morals in these matters but I was too hungry to start an argument.

"What's for supper, darling?" She didn't seem to have heard so I added accusingly, "Beans, Margaret? Isn't it? It's beans?"

She nodded.

"Beans on toast?"

Impishly attractive, she nodded again.

"With a country egg thrown in to jolly well stop you from grumbling," she said.

The change from London had improved her out of all recognition, bringing the colour back to her cheeks, the sparkle to her eyes.

"Margaret," I said, "it's this thoughtful approach of yours to meals that does so much to make our marriage a success."

Then, pretending that the beans were some exotic food, I set to work and gobbled them up.

* 4 *

In the hall Mrs. Biddulph was on her hands and knees in one corner. She came twice a week to help Margaret clean the vicarage. She was what people would call a dear old soul and, although over eighty, worked for the love of it.

What happened was that she would spend a long time in one place with her nose on the ground, but if you were to lift her up, you would find that part of the house where she had been was spotless. The children adored her and imagined she was playing some new kind of game. Taking the polish and rags they would go and burrow in beside her.

Before setting to work Mrs. Biddulph loved to have a long gossip. When Margaret told me some of the things she said about people in the village my hair nearly left its head.

"Have nothing to do with it, Margaret. It's gossip and gossip is dynamite. Don't touch it."

"Don't be silly, Jimmy. It's not malicious."

"I don't care. You know I'm right."

"Unless she has a good chat she doesn't seem able to settle to her work. It's like you missing your morning coffee. And me, I don't pass any comment."

"You have only to make some innocent remark, Margaret, and she to repeat it to the village; before you know where you are it will be 'You know what Mrs. Insight said about so and so, don't you? You mean to say you haven't heard?' A step from that, Margaret, and it's another farewell meeting."

"You're too sensitive, Jimmy. I only listen. Half the time I'm not taking in a word she says, but I will tell you something she has just told me."

"What's that?"

"Mr. Markesete's wife is ill."

"Who's he?"

"He's the landlord at the Cheerful Smile. You ought to call.

48

She doesn't know it, Mrs. Biddulph says, but she's very ill indeed, so just pretend that you dropped in by chance."

"What! At a pub?"

"It's all right in the country."

I was now in a fix. I didn't know which to worry about first; the original problem about Mrs. Biddulph and her gossiping, or this new factor about calling on the landlord and pretending I knew nothing about his wife being ill.

If a parson calls uninvited when there is illness, people get desperately worried thinking he has been tipped off about some incurable disease. Even when he had, it didn't make his job any easier.

"Darling, do stop worrying."

She came close and tried to rub out the creases on my brow, holding them down until I relaxed. She said, "Does it help if I remind you that I was born and bred in a vicarage?"

"Oh that! Margaret, I'd forgotten about that. I think I'll just drop in at the Cheerful Smile this evening and say I like to visit everyone in my parish and want to include them. That wouldn't be a lie, would it?"

"Of course not.

"Do you remember, Margaret, the lady in our last parish who said that it wasn't until you owned a pub that you began to know something about human nature? She said that husbands who came in during the week were quite different from when they came in with their wives at the week end. She said that on their own they were gay and happy, but with their wives they were rather nervy and ill at ease."

"You'll be on your own to-night, darling," she said, "so you can be as gay as you please."

"I wish you'd come," I said, "you'd be much better at finding out what was wrong with Mrs. Markasete, and whether or not she'd like me to visit her."

Just before lunch, Robert took me to see the swan's nest. It was a change for us to go walking together and I found it a stimulating experience.

To reach the nest we had to walk for some way along the tow-path beside the river lying below the glebe. There was coolness coming up from the water and small creatures darted in and out of the rushes. Rounding the corner, we saw the nest situated on the further bank on a piece of land that jutted out into the brown, swirling water. We stood gazing solemnly across at a small portion of the swan's anatomy just visible through the reeds.

Robert had often made this pilgrimage with Mrs. Charmian. She had proved a wonderful friend, helping to rearrange the furniture, advising on shops in the village, and time and again taking care of the children for us. One needed to be careful with Robert, she had told us, because he was apt to become very jealous if he thought that Susan was receiving too much attention; there were times when he ought to be taken out on his own because he was "a big boy". It was from Mrs. Charmian that Robert had picked up snippets of information about swans. These he now imparted to me, telling in his own words how, in due course, one could expect to see the baby swan sitting on its mother's back; that the mother swan, although some thought otherwise, possessed a voice of her own.

I could see now the old bricks, pieces of wood, tins and stones that had been thrown by boys from the village. They were scattered all round the area of the nest. This fascinated Robert and he kept returning to the subject of the "norty boys". It was as if he recognised some primeval instinct in himself that repelled and yet attracted him.

"It's wrong of them, Robert," I said. "If they go on like that, there won't be any baby swans for us to see."

He nodded.

When we had absorbed all that we could of the scene, I was ready to go. Robert, however, had a small piece of bread with him and we had to wait until he could bring himself to throw it into the water, watching to make sure that it would float close enough to the further shore for the mother swan to reach out and scoop it up.

We took the long way home, which brought us out on to the

main road leading into the village. When we reached the road sign that said "St. Hilda's", a man on the other side of the road hailed us. He was pushing an old tricycle, behind which was towed a small cart such as the Bisto Twins might use. I had noticed him in church the previous Sunday and recognised him to be a spastic but had not had the opportunity to talk to him. Now, as we crossed to him, the shaking of his limbs was obvious and it wasn't easy to understand his disorganised speech. After making several abortive attempts to interpret him, I finally came to the conclusion that he was repeating "You are the Lord's anointed." He was delighted at my proximity, nodding his head and putting out a hand to touch my sleeve. I moved my arm close to him so that he could do this without difficulty. Without my dog collar I felt I must have looked a scruffy sort of parson, but this obviously didn't bother him. Like a policeman, it wasn't the man that mattered so much as the authority he represented. Through all of this, I was aware of Robert's intense interest.

After much effort, we gathered that the purpose of the little truck behind the bicycle was to transport a giant marrow that in due course would be offered to me for the Harvest Festival. Once accustomed to the slurred and broken speech and the wild waving of his limbs, it was impossible not to like the man. We said good-bye warmly, assuring him of our friendship, telling him we would watch out for him in church and that we would be looking forward to seeing the marrow.

Some way further on, it became important to Robert to know the man's name; the telling of the story to his mother would be the poorer without it. I felt reluctant to chase after the unfortunate spastic for so seemingly slight a reason, but Robert was adamant and for his sake I did it. It did not entail a great retracing of footsteps. The poor man had not progressed very far beyond the point where we had left him. Far from thinking the reason slight, he appeared delighted that I should have attached so much importance to learning his identity. And when he spoke there was no slurring and no hesitation. He pronounced his name clearly and roundly, giving a startling vision of the man he might otherwise have been.

"Danny."

We were practically home when Robert broke what for him had been a long silence. Almost to himself, and without the condescension that often accompanies such a remark made by an adult, he said, "Poor Danny."

It may be due to my religious upbringing, but I'm never really at ease in pubs. Both in the school football team and the University lacrosse twelve I had been encouraged to try the convivial atmosphere of the public house. The result had not been happy. After attempting to drink a beer, I would sit wretchedly in the motor-coach until the others were ready to return. Later, David tried to assure me that there was nothing really evil about pubs and that a church congregation and a public house gathering have much in common—the same seeking for happiness in companionship, the same husband reluctant to return to his incompatible wife, the same frustrated spinster. I suppose he may have been right. And there's always the lurking fear that the gathering will suddenly break into a rousing chorus of "Knees Up, Mother Brown". It's not only that I don't know the words; I'd never be able to bring myself to join in anyway. All parsons have a different approach to public houses. My own policy has always been to try and keep in touch without giving the impression that I am continually going in or coming out of the licensed houses in my parish. It's a funny thing but no sooner has a parson paid a friendly call, passed the time of day with the locals, imbibed a modest pint of ale or rough cider, than he comes out and runs slap into the most bigoted member of his congregation.

"Ah Mrs. X . . ." he stutters, "how nice to see you. I was just . . ."

Explanations are useless. Her eyes seem to say "At it again! He's at it again!"

Nervously therefore I pushed open the door of the saloon bar of the Cheerful Smile that evening and entered. About four or five men were sitting round the room and one youngish woman was perched, with her legs crossed, on a stool at the bar. She was reading a newspaper.

"Evening sir," said the man behind the bar. I took him to be the landlord.

"Good evening. Could I have a—a cider, please?" I hoped my uncertainty was not too noticeable. If my visit was to appear natural, I should at least know what I wanted.

While the landlord was drawing the cider, the woman looked up from her paper and smiled at me. "Passing through?" she asked pleasantly.

Before I could reply the landlord corrected, "It's our new vicar." Then, as though he'd hardly expected to see me on his premises, "You are, aren't you, sir?"

I nodded and the woman looked at me with new interest. "Good for you," she said. "This is one way of getting to know your parishioners!" She had a well-educated voice, and the cut of her costume was excellent. Her name was Mrs. Atwell, and I could cheerfully have spent the rest of the evening sitting on the stool next to her. She had a way with her—enlisting my aid with her crossword puzzle, steadying my hand as I clumsily attempted to light her cigarette, and getting me to give far more information about myself than I normally did. It was not wasted time, however, as I had opportunity to study Mr. Markesete at close quarters without appearing to do so. When not serving customers, he stood at one end of the bar working out arithmetical problems on a piece of paper. He was middle aged, with a good head of hair and a pleasant face that lacked the flush that one is so often apt to associate with publicans. A vulnerable-looking man, I would have said; one who could easily be hurt. Once, glancing at him, I found him looking at me.

"You know," I said to Mrs. Atwell, "I really ought to move around and speak to some of the others."

"Forget it, enjoy yourself. I'll tell you who they all are."

"That would be cheating."

"Would it? Not if you were here for pleasure. You should relax sometimes, you know. 'All work and no play . . .' I think you should come here again one evening and leave your work behind you."

"Without my dog collar?"

"Without your dog collar." She mimicked. "You're only going to talk to these old codgers out of a sense of duty."

"Oh, no, I——" She was right, in a way, of course. I did have an ulterior motive. "Well, actually, I'm hoping something may happen before I leave."

She looked amused. "How exciting! Are you going to preach a sermon?"

"Good heavens, no."

"A miracle, then? Well ... you're a change from the usual run." She gave me a look. "You may see me at St. Hilda's yet."

I smiled quizzically. "You make *that* sound like a miracle." Sliding from my stool and hoping that the cider wasn't going to my head, I added, "I'd be very pleased to see it come true."

It was interesting, I thought, how intrigued some people became if a clergyman talks to them in a perfectly ordinary fashion without pushing religion at them. I could almost hear Mrs. Atwell thinking "What's his game?"

Terrified at the possibility of a snub, I spoke to the man nearest to the bar. He greeted me with warmth, leaping up and saying that he was the bell-ringer at St. Hilda's.

"This *is* nice, sir," he beamed. "I've been wanting to talk to you ever since you came in, but I didn't dare."

"Why not?" I asked.

"Well, it was the last vicar. He wasn't too keen on the drink, you know, and ..." He smiled happily. "But of course, I can see you're all for it."

I was soon in general conversation with him and his cronies.

In the space of an hour I made four good friends, including the landlord and Mrs. Atwell—and politely declined as many offers of further refreshment. I knew that each of these people would probably pass on details of the encounter to numerous acquaintances and hoped it would all be for the good. But what about my mission? I knew that the man I had mentally labelled "the landlord" was Mr. Markesete, but that was as far as I'd got. I couldn't stay much longer, and I couldn't mention his wife or her illness. While we were talking I'd hoped that one of the others might ask after her, so bringing her into the conversation, but no one did. It looked as though I'd have to come again and go through the same procedure some other evening. I was disappointed but there was no alternative.

Returning to the bar with my glass, I told Mr. Markesete I'd enjoyed the evening.

"Always glad to see you, sir," he said.

I hesitated for a moment, torn with the desire to come out with what was on my mind, then reached across and shook him by the hand. Then I turned to say good-bye to Mrs. Atwell, who had been watching me with a cynical smile.

A chorus of "good-nights" followed me to the door, which I had almost reached when I was conscious of a movement behind me. It sounded as though the bar flap had been raised and lowered. I longed to turn, but couldn't. It was reasonable to suppose that the landlord was merely going to collect the glasses. My hand reached out to the door, and then Mr. Markesete was beside me. He spoke quickly, in an embarrassed undertone.

"I know how busy you are, sir, but if you could spare a moment there's something I'd like to talk to you about. In private, sir, if you wouldn't mind."

As I let him show me through a side door, I glanced quickly in Mrs. Atwell's direction. She was watching us with interest. As she caught my eye, she raised her eyebrows and inclined her head a little to let me know that she recognised this as the "something" I'd hoped might happen. Probably she imagined I was furtively ordering crates of alcohol for secret drinking sessions at the vicarage. Well, she could believe what she liked. I was too thrilled at this unexpected success to care.

It was dark in the passage and I closed my eyes for a few seconds to get used to the gloom. An invisible Mr. Markesete, still speaking in an undertone, said "It's my wife, sir. She's ill in bed."

"I'm sorry to hear that," I murmured.

"It's nothing much. She'll be up and about soon." He paused and then went on rather hurriedly, "It's just that you seemed so at home in there—and she's always been so full of life . . . I wondered if you would care to visit her."

"I'd love to. Can I—now?"

I think he'd expected I would come another day, but he said it would be fine and asked if I'd mind waiting a moment. Then, switching on a light that only slightly relieved the blackness, he went quickly up a flight of stairs at the foot of which we had been standing. Within minutes he reappeared at the head of the stairs and called softly for me to come up.

Across the landing at the top of the stairs, light filtered from a partly open door.

"In here, sir," whispered the landlord, ushering me into the room.

Mrs. Markesete was lying in one half of a double bed, the surprise just leaving her face, a pink bed-jacket bunched in one hand and held before her as though it had been hastily put on. Her husband stayed only long enough to introduce us and find me a chair. Her anxious eyes followed him to the door, almost willing him not to leave her alone with me.

I had time to glance round the room, noticing the rough attempts to modernise it—the wash basin not quite level with the wall, the new carpet, the narrow strip light above the bed.

"It's kind of you to bother," she said nervously as the door closed behind Mr. Markesete. "I hope to be up soon."

"That's good," I replied lightly. "What seems to be the trouble?"

"The doctor said it was something to do with my glands. He wants me to stay in bed a little longer."

"The rest will probably do you good," I said, not wanting to appear to make too much of her illness. "We've only recently come to the village, you know, and I want to get to know as many people as I can."

"Yes, of course . . . Where were you before?"

"London."

"I like London. Not to live. But it's always interesting to visit."

"Yes. There's always something going on."

A burst of laughter from below punctuated our conversational sparring. She was not yet at ease with me and it was heavy going.

"London ..." she said again. "You'll find it very different here."

"I know. That's really why we came. My wife wasn't well in London, but the air here is doing her good already."

She nodded, although that probably wasn't the sort of difference she'd meant. But she obviously wasn't going to pursue the matter. It wasn't worth the effort. So we struggled on, the words between us flat and heavy and doomed. Was this to be the room where the crucifixion would take place? Perhaps her illness was as serious as the gossips made out. Pray God the gossips were wrong; but already, because of their talk, I could smell the stench and feel the pain. It was as though the walls of the room were closing in on the bed, day by day, until it was no more. And she had wanted to see me—of that I was sure. So it could be that she felt it too.

I decided to give it a few more minutes and then go. One couldn't expect to do more than establish contact on the first visit. Maybe I'd make more headway next time—if there was a next time. What if I had disappointed her in some way and she wouldn't want me to call again? I shied away from the thought. Then, apropos of absolutely nothing we had been saying, she suddenly stated, "I was baptised in your church." There was a look of faint surprise on her face, as if the words had been some product of inner compulsion.

"St. Hilda's?" I asked unnecessarily.

"Yes," she replied. The hurdle had been cleared and now she could say what she'd wanted to say. "I've always felt there was —well, something more that needed to be done ..."

"Confirmation?"

"Yes. Is it very difficult to be confirmed?"

"No, not at all. I'll be starting classes soon." I hesitated, but only for an instant. "You could come."

"If I—" She looked up. "Oh, but I will." Her eyes held mine

for a moment. "Supposing I wasn't up when they started . . . is there—I mean, could you . . . ?"

"Well," I said easily, "I don't see why something couldn't be arranged." But it was not easy to keep the excitement from my voice.

5

THERE lived in the vicinity of St. Hilda's two families—the Bresewells and the Raffertys—who, in their own ways, symbolised quite different approaches to village life.

I had been saving the Raffertys for a visit much as a child will save the currants from a rice pudding. General opinion had it that they were not worth visiting. Mr. Bigwood, the last vicar, had tried hard enough without even getting one of them as far as the church porch. The kindest criticisms were that they lived on credit, were shiftless and good-for-nothing, had no morals, and were an open disgrace to the name of St. Hilda's—and if they appeared to be happy, it was the happiness of the brute beast.

In order to reach the family, who lived in the rear quarters of a disused farm, I had to cross two or three fields. It was raining and my shoes squelched noisily in the soft ground. A small slope led down to the Raffertys' ramshackle abode and, anxious to get out of the downpour, I hurried my pace. The bank was more steep than I had expected and I lost my footing, staggered, and slithered rapidly to the bottom, landing flat on my back in the mud. An old woman, wearing deep mourning, gazed down at me expressionlessly.

"No one's at home," she said shortly.

I scrambled to my feet. "May I come in and visit *you*?"

She turned and entered the building without replying. I followed her inside, passing down a number of dark passages out of which ran openings at regular intervals. Above some of these, sacking was nailed to broken plaster and hung down in place of doors.

In a large, smoky room we found three or four children, all of whom looked unwashed and were dressed in filthy, ragged clothes. They were playing some game on the floor, but jumped up as we entered. At the far end of the room a woman sat staring into the grate. I took her to be the children's mother, but she gave no indication that she was aware of them. Neither did she seem to have noticed my arrival. The old woman showed no contrition for having said that no one was at home but shook her head instead, raising her eyes to the ceiling, as if to indicate that all was not well with the woman by the grate.

Beneath the window and almost flush with the floor was a large bed. Up-ended orange boxes served as chairs round a table that was scored in parts as if with a branding iron. In the centre of the table stood a dish of vinegar in which pieces of cucumber floated. It produced an acid but pleasant aroma, having the effect of sharpening the appetite.

Some more children entered the room, so that now there were six or seven. In addition, three young boys arrived—one as big as a man, and another with yellow braces and the bright eyes of a devil. Catching sight of my collar they summed up the situation and disappeared, coming back a little later to watch the proceedings through a broken pane in the window, the rain apparently having stopped.

There was a commotion and a cackling of hens in the passage, followed by the appearance of a husky looking man in brown, shapeless clothes.

"Mr. Rafferty?" I said.

"I was in the village, your riverence, when they brought news that you were visiting our humble lodgings. So I came with all the speed of which I was capable."

He had a manner of speaking that was impressive, as though he had just written the words down. It led one to expect he was going to make a long speech and it came as a surprise when he didn't.

"I've been meaning to visit you for ages," I said.

"I am charmed, indeed, your riverence, that this should have been upon your mind."

He picked up a child at random, swinging her high above his head and back into his arms. She squealed and chuckled excitedly, her grubby frock flying up to reveal that she wore nothing beneath it.

"Our mother is not her full self," he went on. "The arrival of our last child, now asleep in the next room, has caused her to remain very low for some weeks." He turned to the old woman, enquiring politely, "Has our mother said anything to you at all while I have been away in the village?"

"Not a bliddy thing," was the reply.

I asked quickly if I might be allowed to call for the children on Sunday and take them to Sunday School.

This time he did make something of a speech.

"According to your standards, sir, we are not a religious family. We do not attend church, although all the children are baptised as soon as they make their appearance in this world. In our own way, riverence, we live happily because we live freely. We are not concerned with what others say about us. However, since a gentleman like yourself has taken the trouble to come all this way to visit us, we shall be honoured, sir, for you to admit the children as scholars to your school. There is no need for you to call. They will be sent along suitably cleansed and prepared."

The way in which he said the last few words made me think that he recognised his problems but, with an ailing wife, had little stomach for tackling them.

"I'd like to call on Sunday," I said. "That is, if you don't mind. Because I can then introduce the children to the others and settle them into their various classes."

There was a rustle among the children and some stifled sniggering. They must already have known every youngster in the village. The child in Rafferty's arms, hearing the movement of the others and wanting to attract attention, suddenly caught him by the ear, savagely twisting it and crying out. He lifted her frock and smacked her smartly across the buttocks, assuring her that there was plenty more where that came from.

When I left, they all followed me to the door and stood watching me silently as I negotiated the slope and made my way across the wet fields out of their sight.

The soggy ground didn't bother me. I felt buoyant, as though I was walking on air. I'd been far luckier than poor old Bigwood.

All those children for Sunday School—and with no more trouble than slipping over in the mud!

Margaret was having tea in the study when I arrived back at the vicarage. Susan was playing on the rapidly drying path just outside the window and Robert, I was told, had gone down to the village with Mrs. Charmian. I explained to Margaret why I was covered in mud then hurried off to change; wanting to tell her the whole story from the beginning.

She heard me without saying very much, and it occurred to me that she probably knew a great deal more about the Raffertys than I did on account of what was said in the village. Nevertheless, she must have felt that it was a time to humour me and listen to all I had to say. I was full of my success at getting them to promise to come to Sunday School and felt vaguely disappointed at Margaret's lukewarm response. She probably sensed this and was grateful for the hurried knock at the front door that interrupted us. Getting up before I could, she went to answer it. Still churning over plans for the Raffertys, I heard her talking to someone in the hall. Then she called me.

Mrs. Charmian stood just within the door, her eyes anxious and her cheeks flushed. Margaret's face was ashen.

"Robert's lost!"

"Lost?"

"I had him in Bradley's, Vicar," Mrs. Charmian broke in. "One minute he was there, and then when I looked round he was gone. He wasn't in the street. I thought he might have come home by himself, but Mrs. Insight says ... Oh, my goodness, where can he ... ? I don't know what to say ..."

"We must look for him ... quickly. I'll go on my bicycle."

Out in the woodshed I wrenched at the old machine and, pedalling furiously, shot out of the gate. No one could blame Mrs. Charmian. With his short sturdy legs Robert would be well away in no time. But where?

First I scoured the road and the river bank along the route to the swan's nest, but without success. Then I made for the church, calling out to Quimbolt, before cutting through to Mrs. Pankhurst. There was no time to stop long anywhere and, desperately worried, I shot down one alley after another. St. Hilda's was a rabbit warren of back streets and everywhere there were people who already knew what had happened. None of them, however, had seen any sign of Robert.

Cycling wildly back over the ground already covered, I saw Margaret coming towards me with Susan in her pram.

"Any news?" I called.

She shook her head, near to tears.

"I'll try the wishing well. He may be trying to get at the pennies. I'm sure he's all right."

But I wasn't sure; and he wasn't at the wishing well. My heart sank as I turned away to continue the search. Could this be some punishment for my own weak life? "Please, God, let me find him, let me find him before it's too late," I prayed. There was no set course now. It was merely a matter of moving as quickly as possible wherever the roads led me. Then, rounding a corner at a dangerous angle, I saw him ahead of me. He was standing on the pavement looking up at Danny.

Relief flooded me and, as I braked to a wobbly halt, I watched as Robert took the spastic's hand and solemnly shook it. Evidently he was saying good-bye for he turned then and saw me.

"Hullo, Daddy."

"Hullo, Robert," I said unevenly.

"Can we go home now?"

"Yes—yes, let's go." I swung him up on to the cross-bar, feeling his sturdiness beneath the buster suit.

From Danny's fractured speech and gesticulations I gathered that he had just met Robert in the street and knew therefore that I must be near by. I didn't attempt an explanation but thanked him for looking after the child.

Savouring the joy of discovery I took a more leisurely pace homewards. I knew that Margaret would still be desperately anxious, but now I could anticipate her great relief. As we went, I wondered how best to impress upon Robert the seriousness of what he'd done. Now that I'd found him it was hard to be angry.

"Robert, you know you shouldn't have left Mrs. Charmian," I said gently.

He was silent for a moment.

"I was visiting. Like you, Daddy. I was visiting Danny."

We were nearly home and I realised how the Good Shepherd must have felt when he found the sheep that was lost and brought it home rejoicing. Margaret was standing in the road outside the vicarage drive, gazing in the opposite direction. When she turned round it was almost worth losing Robert to see the joy in her eyes. She had him off the cross-bar and wrapped in her arms almost before I'd stopped pedalling.

When Mrs. Charmian came on the scene she caught Robert to her, pressing his head against her skirt.

"Your Mummy and Daddy will never let me take you out again," she said, tears pouring down her cheeks. "*Never.* I know they won't."

On the Sunday, I went for the Rafferty children. After banging on the door for what seemed an age I heard the shuffling of feet. The door opened a fraction and the old woman peered at me suspiciously.

"Good morning," I said brightly. "The children. I've called for them."

"*Have* you?"

"Yes, are they ready?"

"I don't know."

"Never mind. I have a few minutes to spare. I can wait."

She disappeared and I stood humming a little tune. After a while I put my head through the aperture made by the half closed door. She was coming back along the passage.

"They've got chicken-pox."

"Chicken-pox? But . . . Are you sure?"

"Positive."

"It's just that—well, they seemed all right during the week."

"Well, they're not now."

"Do they all have it?"

"The whole bliddy lot." She was looking me straight in the eye, unblinking.

"I'm sorry . . . If they have chicken-pox, there's not much point in my calling again for some weeks."

"No," she said, closing the door firmly.

There was no such problem about getting the Bresewells into church. Every Sunday they filled up almost three of our small pews, following the service with great enthusiasm, their books held out before them.

In church Mr. Bresewell wore a black suit and carried a bowler, standing in the aisle as his family filed into their places with the hat held out as if to bar entry to intruders. On week-days, however, he wore other clothes—an alarming suit of bottle green which he topped with an equally alarming brown pork-pie hat. He had a purplish face from which a monocle glinted and winked according to the position of the sun, and practically all of his upper lip was fringed by a thick moustache. Although the owner of three expensive motor-cars, he liked to drive through the country lanes in a pony and trap.

As I was about to leave the vicarage on my first visit to the family, Margaret stopped me.

"If you get the opportunity, Jim, don't forget to ask Mr. Brese-well if he knows of any part-time teaching jobs."

She had heard that he had once been an inspector of schools and might therefore know of something in the vicinity. Our financial situation, aggravated by the expenses of our move from London, was becoming rather tricky. Money is the bane of most parsons, and even where the P.C.C. has some to spare very few will ask for personal help from that source. One has to look for other means. St. Paul, faced with a similar problem, had turned again to his tent-making. I would try to teach.

It was past normal tea-time when I arrived at the Bresewells' but they were just about to start a meal, to which I was wel-comed. The place of honour, to the right of Mrs. Bresewell, was given to me, and Mr. Bresewell said grace in a very pleased voice

3+

while the family stood behind their chairs with folded hands. There seemed to be even more children than at the Raffertys', but here they were mostly well into their 'teens.

The small hush following grace was broken by the scraping of chairs on the red tiled floor of the farm kitchen as we sat down at the giant mahogany table. Mr. Bresewell began to carve a large round of beef, talking away at the same time. He spoke confidently and exuberantly on almost every subject covered by the religious alphabet. All his remarks were addressed to me, although from time to time he would shoot a question at one or other of the members of his family. Meanwhile the young people kept themselves busy passing back and forth some of the cut-glass bowls of salad, earthenware dishes of potatoes and squat jugs of orange juice with which the table was littered.

"You're a converted man, Vicar," Mr. Bresewell stated, having just touched upon the subject of conversion. "I can tell that from your sermons."

I murmured an affirmative.

"When did it happen?" he pressed me. "Your conversion, I mean. When were you born again?"

"Some time ago now. It was at a tent mission."

"Good. Good. These tent missions are great stuff." He pointed with the carving knife. "All my brood are converted, Vicar, every one of them. They can all tell you the date, the place, even perhaps the time. All, that is, with one exception . . ." I watched, fascinated, as the carving knife moved along the ranks, pointing at last to where a small dark girl with pigtails turned crimson. "Our baby, Veronica, Vicar. But she's coming along. It won't be long now, will it, eh, Veronica?"

All eyes were on the poor embarrassed child as she whispered tremulously, "No, Father."

"Now then, Vicar," Bresewell went on, dismissing Veronica but not conversion, "what about that warden of yours—Charrington-Hawes? Is he a converted man? I've prayed for him for years."

I coughed and sipped my orange juice. This was the type of discussion one tried to side-step. It was wrong of him to question me in this manner about the spiritual position of someone else. What's more, one was sure that no answer would really satisfy him if he'd already made up his own mind.

The arrival of the desserts saved an awkward situation. There were bowls of trifle, jelly, luscious-looking tarts and thick cream, and these were spread at our end of the table so that Mrs. Bresewell could do the serving. In the ensuing clatter conversation slowed to a temporary halt. Taking advantage of the lull, I ignored the question about Charrington-Hawes and asked instead about part-time teaching.

Side-tracked, Bresewell answered me with the air of a man forced to talk about something in which he had no great interest.

"Surely you know Thomas, in your own choir! He's principal of a college in County Town. No doubt he'll be able to fix you up." Then he was off again on a monologue about texts he wished interpreted, conventions held in near-by villages and the unspiritual effect of television on the populace as a whole.

Listening with one ear, and making occasional noncommittal sounds, I tried to study the silent family. Was this their daily lot, and what effect did it have on them? They seemed to be battered to silence by the unceasing flow of words. Were they listening, or were they thinking private thoughts as the sound of their father's voice washed around and over them? He was now launched on a talk he hoped to give at some distant Bethel on Sunday evening.

"What do you think of it, Vicar? Does it strike the right note? It's the gospel, naturally—because no matter what these villagers say, many of them are hardened sinners, Vicar, and there's no doubt about it."

"Can I give you a little more trifle, Mr. Insight?" Mrs. Bresewell's voice made me start, despite the quietness of her tone.

"Thank you," I said, turning to her gratefully. "It's really marvellous. Did you make it yourself?"

Pleased at the unexpected compliment, she began to reply. Her husband, however, had not finished talking and it was possible to feel the uneasiness around the table at the interruption. As her spoon dipped towards the bowl, it became afflicted with a slight tremor. When she had served me, she looked down the table.

"Trifle, dear?" she said.

"I'm still eating."

It wasn't the words so much as the brusque way in which they were said that caused her to colour violently and sit patiently waiting. The tension was tangible. If she should ever snap, I thought, Mr. Bresewell will one day find himself getting his trifle without the benefit of a plate. But I was thankful it didn't happen during my visit.

"He sounds pretty grim," said Margaret, when I told her about the visit.

"It was the children who worried me," I said, "they all seemed too scared to join in the general conversation. They appeared to be frightened of their own father! Of course he's a Victorian and they have the oddest ideas about family life."

"You ought to have played up and tried to bring them all into the picture."

"His wife seemed scared as well," I said.

"With lots of people in a family it isn't terribly easy to know how to lay down the law. And if the children are teenagers things can quickly get out of hand. You get the children telling you what to do if you're not careful. I wonder how we'll manage when Robert and Susan grow up. It's bad enough at the moment with their quarrelling but at least you can put them to bed if they're too impossible. You can't do that with teenagers, Jimmy."

"I know. And it's almost as bad if you get extreme anti-Victorianism. I think I'd rather have that though than a cowed and silent group. It's more natural. There's more hope for development of ideas. I think that if the parents try and lay down the law on a fairly broad scriptural basis and pray about their children then that is all they can do. But either way is full of problems. You know, I feel awfully pessimistic. What *are* we to do?"

"What about a nice middle way, darling? Not too easy going or too strict?"

"Suits me."

That same evening I was due to call on Mrs. Markesete. She was up for the first time, sitting in a chair beside the bed and looking painfully thin. She said, "You do believe I'll recover, Vicar, don't you?"

"You mustn't be in too great a hurry," I replied. "Just do whatever the doctor says."

She looked away. "Doctors aren't always right, you know."

"Well—the rest can't do you any harm."

"Rest!" she said bitterly. Her lips quivered and I was afraid she might burst into tears.

We were no longer strangers. Four classes had now been completed, informal chats really, in which I had spoken about God's great love in Christ for the sinner. She had responded and I'd had the impression that she looked forward to my calls. But this time I could feel her antipathy. It was something for which there was no explanation. Like wavelengths on the wireless so it is with people. With some one can tune in within a matter of moments. With others it is almost an impossibility. With Mr. Markesete, for example, I felt at ease at once. With his wife never. But because she was the opportunity for my being able to carry out what I was supposed to be doing, the work of a pastor, I was grateful. Her own antipathy may have been due to this wavelength business or it could have been the jealous reaction of a person who is ill towards one who, at the moment, is well, and can bound out from the sickroom into the sunlight and air. Cooped up in her bedroom day after day, she would have been a saint not to have had moments of despair and irritation.

Whenever he could spare a moment from the bar, her husband would come and join us. On this occasion I was more glad to see him than ever, hoping his presence might induce a change of mood. The hope was short-lived.

"Jack," she said as he entered the room, "I'm going to get

better, aren't I? Perhaps you can convince the Vicar." Her voice became brittle. "I don't think he believes I will."

"Of course you will, my love. The Vicar thinks so, too. I *know* you'll get better, and I'll prove it to you. Do you know what I'm going to do? I'm going to buy a new car—and in two weeks' time I'll drive you through St. Hilda's. You'll look like a queen. And we'll go to the sea. That's what we'll do—we'll go to the sea."

"Hear that, Mr. Insight? A new car. And we'll go to the sea." She was on the verge of tears. "I think I'll go back to bed now and have a little sleep."

It was my dismissal and I accepted it, promising to come again soon and waiting out on the landing while her husband attended to her.

The publican took me downstairs and escorted me through the bar, apologising unnecessarily for this as he always did. In the road we stood beneath the swinging sign of the Cheerful Smile.

"Thank you for coming, sir, and I'm sorry if it was a waste of time to-night."

"It's never a waste of time, Mr. Markesete, I'm sorry that your wife . . . Do you think she should have been out of bed?"

"I don't know, sir. I really don't know." He looked desperately unhappy. "She wanted to get up and I—and I—well, I couldn't refuse her . . . I just want her," his voice broke, "to be as—as happy as possible . . ."

Wondering how much he knew about his wife's illness and conscious that I had only my own instincts to guide me, I wished him good-night and sadly shook his hand.

★ 6 ★

ENJOYING the light and colour of the evening, I set out early for the Parochial Church Council Meeting. It was a time for making the most of the glorious weather. The meetings were quarterly affairs, and when the next one came round winter would be upon us. But that was not my only reason for an early start. For one thing, I wanted to be sure that Quimbolt had everything ready in the church hall. Mostly, however, I wanted to mull over my plan to suggest at this gathering that we inaugurate a fund for the interior decoration of St. Hilda's.

Just beyond the lychgate, I came across an easel set up in the middle of the church path. A girl was standing back from it, a paint brush held out at arm's length. I stopped to admire her work.

"That's extremely good."

She jumped at the sound of my voice and turned to face me.

"Oh! You *did* give me a shock. I didn't hear you coming ... Thank you—for the compliment, I mean."

Her hair was the shade of burnished bronze that only nature could produce and it framed a high-cheekboned, vitally individual face—rather reminiscent of a young Katherine Hepburn. An extraordinarily attractive girl.

"You seem rather—rather young to paint so well," I said.

She laughed and pushed some stray hairs from her brow. "A fault soon cured!"

"Really, though. You've caught that perfectly. It's almost like a coloured photograph of the church. I—I wish I could afford to buy it when it's finished."

"How encouraging you are! But I'm afraid it won't be for sale. At least, not by me. It's going to be a gift, and if you really wanted to buy it you'd have to ask the Vicar."

"But I *am* the Vicar," I said.

"Oh? Oh!" She blushed and bit her lip; then she giggled. "You could have fooled me! I was expecting you to be much older." With her head on one side, she studied me as if not quite convinced. "I've heard something about you."

"I know. That wretched newspaper report."

"No, not that. This is something else—rather interesting. I'd love to ask you about it, if you wouldn't mind."

"I don't know what it could be—but go ahead."

"Not now. I'm sure you're on your way somewhere, and this would take some time. If you could spare a few minutes one day, I've recently set up a little studio behind the mill. I don't actually live there but I spend a great deal of time there. Does that make me one of your parishioners?"

"I suppose it might," I replied, willing to stretch a point. "In which case, I must call on you. At the moment I'm on my way to a meeting of our church council. I'd like to get them to agree to raise money for renovating the church. Keep your fingers crossed for me."

"Oh, I will. It's a lovely church, but it certainly needs doing up."

"And thank you," I said as I started to move on, "for the promise of that lovely painting."

"Oh, *that!*" She glanced away, self-consciously. Then, as I passed her, she smiled and held up two crimson-tipped fingers crossed one above the other.

Among the members of the P.C.C. were some familiar faces that I'd expected to see—Charrington-Hawes, Farmer Jones, Mr. Bresewell, Mr. Saigon and Major Icely. Sir Henry Triscombe, the treasurer, was still something of a mystery man as far as I was concerned. The meeting took its normal course with the reading and signing of the minutes. Then a number of simple proposals were put forward, such as the need for new Communion linen, more hymn-books and the repair of a broken pew that had nearly caused injury to a parishioner. The bell-ringers' outing was touched upon, and mention was made of our contributions to the magazine which we shared with a number of surrounding villages. Country folk seemed even longer coming to the point than the townee, but the atmosphere generally was friendly. If I sensed a certain caution in their attitude towards me it was, I suppose, understandable in view of the bad start I had unintentionally made with them.

When I mentioned Saigon's proposal for a peace service he stood up himself, speaking as if I were fully in favour of his suggestion. He held the floor for some fifteen minutes, during which time I gazed round the hall and wondered if it too could be included in my redecoration scheme.

"... and I propose, therefore," Mr. Saigon's voice cut across my thoughts, "that St. Hilda's gives its full support to the holding of the annual service of our Peace Movement in our much-loved church."

There was no opposition, and Saigon sat down beaming happily. The smile he gave me as I rose to make my own suggestion had more than a hint of I-told-you-so in it.

"I wonder," I began nervously, "if the time has not come for us to renovate the interior of our church. It is a beautiful building and visitors are in and out of it during the summer months. Having it smartened up would be a tonic for us all. It hardly seems right that we should decorate our own houses yet neglect the house of God and allow it to become more and more dirty as the years go by."

There was an immediate stiffening in the meeting and I hastily switched from implied criticism to an elaboration of the things I had in mind, even to possible colour schemes for different parts of the building. It is difficult to stop talking when the words spring from one's own natural enthusiasm rather than from a set speech. I seemed unable to stop the flow. When at last I did finish, Charrington-Hawes took over.

"Admirable as the vicar's suggestion may be," he said in a pleasant voice, "I think it should be borne in mind that it is not so long since a considerable sum was spent on putting the church bells to rights. It was before his time, so we could hardly expect him to know that. A scheme such as he has in mind would involve considerable expense. I doubt if, at this time, it

3*

would be advisable to embark on such an undertaking. However, it is up to the meeting to make its own decision." He spoke with a quiet authority that made me feel gauche and inexperienced. Before resuming his seat, he added a rider. "The summer visitors referred to by the vicar, incidentally, have always expressed their greatest delight in our church."

My heart sank as Farmer Jones followed, stating in a thick country burr that although enamoured of the suggestion he too felt it was not a thing to rush into. "We wouldn't want to do anything that would alter the character of the church, for instance. In London, of course, there are lots of new churches that look like public libraries from the outside. I'm sure the vicar doesn't mean anything like that, but even so it would take quite a bit of money to decorate the church in keeping—and money is not so easily come by."

A voice I recognised answered this cheerfully. "We have a thousand pounds in the kitty, haven't we?" It was Major Icely.

There was consternation, and everyone looked at Sir Henry Triscombe. Two large ledgers were balanced across his knees and a thick gold chain rose and fell rhythmically and gently across his crumpled waistcoat. He seemed quite unperturbed. "Umm, yes," he said coolly. "It must be something in that region. The hall, you remember, was let at one time to the military. Interest has accrued on the capital received."

"It was on the amount of interest accruing that I made my deductions," said Icely. "It's all in the church accounts. Now how about using our nest egg? I'm in full agreement with the vicar. The church is badly in need of redecoration—and has been for a long time."

Grateful as I was for his support, I intervened to explain that I had not intended the use of such valuable reserves. "I thought we might try to raise some money for the purpose."

"There's no reason," said Charrington-Hawes, "why the matter shouldn't be given some thought."

There was little doubt, however, about the outcome. With Charrington-Hawes and Farmer Jones lined up against me the motion was defeated with the suggestion that it should be proposed again and thoroughly discussed at the next meeting in three months' time. Bitterly disappointed, I took what comfort I could from those who stayed behind to shake my hand and say how much they agreed with my plan.

I was in no hurry to go home and break the news to Margaret. She had been so sure that everyone would share our enthusiasm for giving the church a "new" look. So I took the devious route back that led past Mrs. Pankhurst's house. The light was still on in her hall and I suppose I must have known that I was going to knock on her door. Perhaps she'd known it too, for she showed no surprise to find me on her doorstep.

"I'm feeling depressed," I said. "My plan for doing up the church has been turned down."

"Ah, well. There's always another day, Vicar. Come along inside."

She led me into the kitchen, where I was leapt on by two dogs. When they had been shooed to their respective corners she said, "I could have saved you this disappointment, I suppose."

"How?"

"By suggesting that you wait for a few more months before putting forward your proposal."

"Oh," I said gloomily. "I don't know that that would have made any difference."

"I do. For two reasons. The first is that they still need time to recover from that newspaper nonsense. And the second is that because you're new they resent you telling them the church is dirty."

"Yes, I felt that—but the church *is* dirty."

"Of course it is! Not as dirty, though, as this room. Nor as untidy." She rummaged about on the table. "Just the same, you wouldn't tell me so—and I wouldn't like it if you did. I can criticise my own house, but if *you* did I'd be offended."

"It's my church."

"In a manner of speaking, yes. But it's their church too. They're the sitting tenants and you're the new landlord." She started to busy herself at the stove. "This is the country, not London. If only you'd waited a few more months and then got someone else to put up the proposal—even rather pooh-poohed the suggestion—you'd have had them all eating out of your hand."

"But that wouldn't be honest—and it shouldn't be necessary. It makes the whole thing sound political."

"Well, of *course* it's political!" She held the kettle up in both hands. "It's all political. What else did you expect?"

"I don't know . . . but not politics. I'm no politician."

"You may not be yet. But you will. You'll have to be."

"Oh, dear!" I sighed, sitting down at the table. "You ought to be on the P.C.C., Mrs. Pankhurst. You'd be grand. And so good for my morale. You'd counteract the feeling I get that they're watching and waiting for me to make some slip." I paused for a moment to sort out my thoughts. "Perhaps it wasn't fair of me to say that. It isn't that I expect everyone to agree unreservedly with everything I say and do. I don't. But I'd like to feel that any opposition was entirely without prejudice." I sighed again. "If only they could all be like the Major."

"Did you say the Major?" she asked quietly as she brought my cup of tea to the table.

"Yes."

"And which Major would that be?"

"Is there more than one? I meant Major Icely."

Placing the cup and saucer on the table she arranged it carefully, close to my elbow, taking her time as she said, "He supported you, did he?"

"Yes. But in any event I think he's a wonderful person."

"Do you? I'm glad." She brought her own tea to the table and sat down. "He is a—a very fine man."

"And that house of his! It's really marvellous. If only he . . ." I stopped myself and made a great business of stirring my tea.

"Yes?" she coaxed.

"Nothing . . . The house impressed me immensely."

"If only he what?" she persisted.

She must have known what I'd been about to say, but I think she wanted to actually hear me say it. Although I felt I knew her very well indeed, it occurred to me that there was much about Mrs. Pankhurst that was a closed book to me. For instance there must once have been a Mr. Pankhurst. What sort of man had he been? Someone, I would have thought, with many of the same sterling good qualities of Major Icely. It may have been that thought that prompted me to continue.

"I probably shouldn't say it, but I think that what he needs is a good wife. He ought to be married."

"Ah!" Her face glowed, and the eyes behind the thick lenses seemed to shine. "Yes . . . yes, indeed." Then she jumped up abruptly and hurried to the cupboard, wrenching open the door so that a number of tins cascaded to the floor. Picking up one of them, she brought it back to the table. "I've had this since last Christmas, Vicar. Chocolate biscuits. Let's have a little feast, shall we? Just you and I."

* 7 *

THE winter now with us was the winter of my innocence. Memory is reputedly short and it seemed that at last the villagers had forgotten my unfortunate remarks about their spiritual state. Each day brought its own happiness and it was often difficult to believe that there had ever been any anxiety over Margaret's health. She looked wonderfully well, and that alone justified the move from London. In the matter of the P.C.C. and my redecoration proposal she had been encouragingly philosophical, convinced that I would eventually win them over and that a few more months wouldn't make much difference. For my part, there was no time for brooding about it. I was now a part-time teacher, Thomas having welcomed me to his college. This meant extra money, and with it the ability to meet our living expenses. Not that it was money easily earned. The job presented difficulties that, without the aid of the principal, might have made it impossible.

Thomas was a quiet-spoken, grey-haired man. He had two great loves: the college he commanded—a gloomy building now dedicated to the science of electrical and mechanical engineering —and the choir of St. Hilda's, in which he sang. Under his guidance, I struggled to teach English for four well-paid hours a week. The syllabus was simple—essays and précis, with questions designed to make the students discuss their scientific knowledge on paper in a clear and lucid way.

Throughout the winter I wrestled with two classes of thirty or more pupils whose ages ranged from sixteen to nineteen. All I required of them was silence and their full attention during lesson periods. But there were always elements determined to prevent me having either at any cost. It was the universal problem facing all teachers and, with teaching qualifications but none of the benefits of a teachers' training course, I was undoubtedly less equipped than most to deal with it. Was there much that one could do anyway about a sustained effort to break the teacher's spirit? What was the remedy for the deliberate dropping of books and pencils, the series of low humming sounds that would issue consecutively from various parts of the class, the rising to open or close windows without permission—"I was feeling faint, sir" or "I was in a draught, sir"—the sniggers and unidentifiable but audible remarks the moment one's back was turned? The constant effort to keep order was tiring yet stimulating, causing the brain to search frantically for ways in which to combat the enemy—for one came to look upon them as such. Nevertheless it was something more than a game. It would be interesting to take a census of mental institutions and find out how many of the inmates were once full-time schoolteachers. Some form of schoolboy rebellion against discipline has always existed. It was once nothing more than just high spirits, but in recent times it seems to have become more openly defiant, aggressive, and even brutal. The press was full of the problem—the problem of a growing race determined to know no authority—the problem of my own village, where the police were constantly investigating complaints of wanton damage by children. Dealing with an assortment of youngsters *en masse* was sometimes more than I felt I could cope with.

On one occasion, after a particularly noisy session, I made my way dispiritedly to the principal's study. Sinking into an armchair by his desk, I poured out my pent-up feelings.

"It doesn't seem to be any use. I want the boys to like and trust me. Instead, they seem to resent me—maybe because they know I'm a clergyman. Whatever it is, it looks as though I'm a failure. I think the best thing would be for me to resign."

Thomas was wonderful. He listened gravely, fingers together, lips pursed, until I had finished. Then he leaned forward to touch a tape recorder that lay open on his desk. "Vicar, we intend buying this recorder for the college and I've been testing it. There's something on it I'd like you to hear." He switched it on and there was a whirring sound as the machine warmed up. Then quite suddenly I heard my own choir singing "Lord, now lettest Thou Thy servant depart in peace". Lying back in the chair, I closed my eyes.

When it was over I rose and said softly, "Thank you ... I think I'd better get off home now. I'm sorry to have bothered you."

"Not at all. That's what I'm here for." He walked with me to the door. "That top class of yours—it's one of the most difficult we've had." He smiled. "If you can handle that class, you can handle anyone—even grown-ups."

"I feel better about it now, sir. You've helped me tremendously." And I really did feel better, determined to redouble my efforts to win the class over. It seemed the right note on which to leave, and I opened the door. As I did so, Thomas laid his hand on my arm.

"Incidentally, Vicar, I'm sure they don't resent you. On the contrary, some of them quite like you."

The degree to which a clergyman brings his family into contact with his parishioners is something he has to work out for himself. I wanted my family to know as many of mine as possible and, during the winter months, we called on various members of the congregation.

We saw much of Mrs. Charmian, almost pressing her to look after Robert in order that she should know we didn't blame her for the day he was lost. Sometimes she would have both the children for a whole day, and they would have a glorious time in her charming little house overlooking the river.

Charrington-Hawes invited us to his home on a number of occasions. He was extremely wealthy, his house and grounds so large that one expected to be met on the steps by a man selling tickets for a conducted tour. In the drawing room, his wife would produce toys that had once belonged to her son for Robert and Susan to play with while she and Margaret talked. Meanwhile, Charrington-Hawes would bear me off to the library. There was always some small matter about which he was not too happy and about which he wanted to know my intentions. Although we would reach agreement, it was never without reservations on his part. He was an older man than I and I valued his advice on church matters, but I would have liked to feel that he had more confidence in me. The reason was, of course, that he had been brought up to govern, to form a judgment and to act on it, and he was unaccustomed to having his opinions disputed. I had not enjoyed these advantages but I had learned to hold to a belief I thought to be right. I could be mulishly obstinate in the face of determined opposition, however sincere it may be. And sincerity and integrity were two qualities no one could deny in this handsome man to whom any form of indecision was patently foreign.

The library itself had a rather overpowering effect. The walls were lined from floor to ceiling with well-stocked bookshelves containing, from a brief glance at some of the titles, the best in English literature. It was frightening to think of all the time that would be needed to read one's way through the collection. The illusion remained even after the time I'd been left alone in there for a few minutes. Looking along the shelves, I'd reached for a volume of Tennyson's poems. To my amazement, five other leather bound volumes had come out with it in a solid block. Where the leaves of the book should have been there was nothing but hollow wood.

Jeremiah Jones and his wife were much less awe-inspiring people. He had a way with children and delighted in taking Robert and Susan all over his farm. While he was with them he became a child again himself—standing in awe before the bull pen, snorting at the pigs, fondling the lambs, chasing the geese. It was a good, well-run farm and Jones said that if he did not come to church twice on Sundays it was because, in his eyes, it was not Christian to sit in church while his labourers had to do his stint on the farm. He seemed to have great consideration for his work-people and, in fact, for everyone with whom he came into contact. When I wished to scythe my little glebe he sent a man to do it for me, and he advised me personally on how to set about keeping bees.

Just before Christmas a large hamper arrived at the vicarage. The children, wild with excitement, wanted us to open it at once despite the fact that Margaret and I were having tea in the study

with Mrs. Pankhurst, who had called to discuss the Christmas
decorations.

"Later," I said. "There's plenty of time. Run along and play
now."

Susan might have given in but Robert was not to be put off.
"Now," he insisted. "Let's see now."

Here were all the makings of one of our not infrequent scenes
with Robert, but Mrs. Pankhurst intervened.

"Oh, do let them, Vicar. It would be absolute torture for them
to have to wait."

So the hamper was opened, disclosing provisions fit for a king.
Apples, oranges, grapes, a giant pineapple, nuts, pickles, a leg of
pork, a turkey, raisin wine. It was so packed that all the wonderful things could be seen sitting in separate compartments with
none of the usual shavings and profusion of paper. A small card
informed us that the gift was from the Joneses.

"Well," I managed, when the exclamations of the others had
died down, "isn't this splendid? I must write at once and thank
them. They really are among the most helpful people one could
ever wish to meet."

Mrs. Pankhurst leaned forward and picked up the pineapple. Examining it, she spoke as if to herself. "I've known
the Joneses all my life. They *are* kind, and they're the same to
everyone. I've sometimes thought them narrow in their views,
but they're true practising Christians."

Margaret and I, thrilled with the magnificence of the gift,
heartily endorsed her last remark.

During the late afternoon of Christmas Eve I went to see
Mrs. Markesete. In a few more hours the church would enjoy
the excitement of its carol service and midnight Communion, but
in the bedroom there was an air of hopelessness pointed rather
than hidden by the few Christmas decorations.

There was no doubt now that Mrs. Markesete was declining,
and I knew with miserable certainty that she would not recover.
She knew it too. Her face seemed to have fallen in and her eyes
were dull with bitter knowledge. We had barely exchanged the

customary seasonal greetings when she said, "What happens when you die?"

"I don't know."

Her fingers moved impatiently on the coverlet. "Isn't it your duty to know?"

"I wish I did know."

"Well, what do you *think* happens?" she persisted.

"Life in another dimension."

"For everyone?"

"Yes."

"All of them happy?"

I shook my head.

"Then you believe in hell?"

"Of course."

She thought about this. "And just by believing in Christ we can go to heaven? Isn't that what you've said?"

I nodded. "That's what I've tried to explain. There are three promises—repentance, faith, obedience. You have to take them for yourself."

There was a pause. Then she said, "Don't you ever doubt?"

"Most of the time."

"Then that means you are not really a Christian."

"It means that I have to fight my doubts—try to have faith."

Her eyes wandered towards the window and she seemed to be fighting some inner battle. When she looked at me again she said, "Am I to be confirmed or not?"

"It's up to you. I would like you to be, very much indeed. If the thought of getting to the church is worrying you, I can assure you that the service could be held right here in this room."

She was tired now, lifting her hand and dropping it on the counterpane. "It's no use. I can't believe all you tell me. I've tried —but I just can't believe it, that's all. And what difference does it make? I don't believe, and you say you have doubts. So what's the difference between us? Tell me that."

"Only that I've taken the promises. I don't think you have."

"But I could pretend that I have. I could be confirmed like that, couldn't I? Lots are."

"Unfortunately, yes."

"I wouldn't though. I'm sick of pretending."

The pain took hold of her then and there was nothing I could do but take my leave of her with a mumbled "Happy Christmas" that seemed to stick in my throat.

Down in the bar, a number of customers were grouped round the piano singing "God and sinners reconciled". Mr. Markesete, twisting a cloth inside a glass, was listening to them. He seemed to be lost in the sound of the voices, but when he saw me he put down the glass and hurried forward to escort me to the door.

With the passing of the months the weather became milder and the young swans reached the stage where they must soon begin to take their first trusting steps towards the water. It was at this point that the thing we had forgotten to fear actually happened.

Looking out of the study window one morning, I saw Mrs. Charmian running up the drive. Her face was working strangely and my heart turned over, the first thought being that some accident had come upon the children. Dashing to the door, I threw it open.

"Oh, Vicar! Quick, quick!" She stumbled and almost fell against me. "It's those ruffians ... they're killing the swans ... Oh, quickly ... do something. Please do something!"

Not waiting to hear any more, and still in my slippers, I raced down to the river bank—through the raspberry canes, over the stile, and out along the path. Praying to God that I would not be too late, I shot round the bend. The nest was still some way ahead but, as I ran, I could see ahead of me what I took to be two or three cygnets. They were lying on their side, motionless. The mother swan was sinking back, one wing spread in a great arc as if she had been trying to shield her small family.

I ran on for some distance, but there was no sign of the attackers. A movement in the fields to my right may have been fancied, though an intervening ditch and a thick hedge would have prevented me from doing much about it anyway. One of my slippers fell off and, as I stooped to put it on, I noticed

something lying in the mud of the river bank. It was a crudely
made catapult with a deep "R" carved in the handle. Holding
it in my hand, I stood looking across at the swan's island. Huge
pieces of bark and large bricks were lying near the bodies. A
helpless frustrated anger shook me. Then the mother swan
moved slightly and, realising that there might be hope for her,
I began to run back to the house.

Margaret was giving Mrs. Charmian a cup of tea in the study,
while Robert played on the floor with my stapling machine.
They all looked up as I burst in and made straight for the
telephone.

"What——" began Margaret. Then, noticing that something
was wrong, she picked Robert up and carried him from the
room.

First I phoned the police station, and was told that they would
look into the matter. Then I got on to the vet.

"Don't worry, sir," said a cheerful voice. "It may not be as
bad as you think. Swans are hardy creatures and they may not
all be dead. I'll take the van through the fields as close as I can
and see to everything."

"Thank you," I said. "We've always dreaded that something
like this would happen."

"Whassat?" came the voice. "Dreadful business? Certainly, sir
—but much more common these days than you might think."

I replaced the receiver and said to Mrs. Charmian, "It looked
as if most of them were dead."

"However will you tell Robert?"

"I don't know."

Margaret came back into the room and I told her what I had
found.

"Oh, Jim! How awful!"

"It's terrible," said Mrs. Charmian. "And I feel so awful,
Vicar—almost as though it were my fault. You see, if only I'd
been a few minutes earlier I might have been able to stop it."

"You mustn't think like that," Margaret comforted her. "How
could you possibly know what was going to happen?"

"Well, I was coming along by the river and I heard these

thuds. At first I thought nothing of it; then suddenly it dawned on me what was happening. By the time I arrived at the spot, though, all I could hear was the children running away. The damage was already done and my first thought was to come for you." She hesitated, then blurted out, "I shouldn't say it, but I think the Rafferty boys were mixed up in this . . . It was one of the jerseys . . . the colour of it . . . I caught a glimpse . . ."

I showed her the catapult so that she could see the letter "R" in the handle. "It doesn't make much odds now who did it. It won't bring the swans back to life. I'll give this to the police." Her lips began to tremble, like a child's. "Don't distress yourself, Mrs. Charmian," I continued. "You did all that you possibly could. You're feeling the reaction now."

"I suppose that's what it is. I think I'd better go now." She rose unsteadily, handing me her empty teacup. This alone was proof that she was not her usual self. Normally she would go out of her way to prevent me so much as lifting a teaspoon. Her face was chalk white and she clutched gratefully at Margaret's proffered arm.

When they had gone, I picked up the stapling machine from the floor. Robert had pulled it to pieces. He'd done it before and had been warned about doing it again. At any other time I would have been furious, but now it didn't seem to matter. All I could think of was the inhumanity of the village boys and what could be done about it.

Sitting at my desk, I stared at a framed photograph of Margaret without really seeing it. What could I do? What *could* I do? On the blotter lay my pen. I picked it up idly and started doodling. The doodles began to take the form of words— "savagery", "hooligans", "destruction"—and I knew then what I could do. Pulling forward some notepaper I wrote a letter to the *County Times*. Once started, it didn't take long. I felt so strongly about what I had to say that the letter practically wrote itself.

Without mincing words, I suggested that the people of St. Hilda's should take another look at the beauty of their village. *Year after year*, I wrote, *visitors come to admire the ancient church, the narrow streets, the thatched houses and the glorious countryside. To me, and perhaps to many others, it has been Honeymoon Village. Is it not time, then, that we who live in the village should face the truth?—that such beauty can be no more than the grin on the face of a skull since it hides the horror of undisciplined children—children who can throw builders' bricks across quiet waters and in a moment blot out a harmless feathered family.* I finished by asking when these little savages were going to receive their just deserts. *What do the people of St. Hilda's intend to do about such behaviour?*

When Margaret returned from saying good-bye to Mrs. Charmian I handed her the letter saying, "Will it do?"

"Who's it to?"

"The *County Times*."

She read it through carefully before making any comment. "I don't want to discourage you, but I suppose you've thought of the possible repercussions."

"I haven't thought of anything but getting this off my chest."

"Well, you've certainly done that, darling—but people aren't going to like it."

I took the letter back from her. "I haven't thought of whether they would or wouldn't. All I want to do is wake them up to their responsibility in the matter."

"I know that, but we haven't exactly been fortunate with newspapers, have we?"

"This is different, Margaret. There's nothing ambiguous here, nothing that could be misinterpreted. It says exactly what I feel— and no one could deny the truth of it. But if you tell me not to post it, I won't. Though what I'd like to do is go out and pop it straight in the box before my cowardly heart recants."

A woman is said to have greater intuition than a man and it's possible that Margaret could see further ahead than I. Had I not been so worked up about things I might have been influenced by her cautious attitude. As it was, my mind was virtually made up and I believe she sensed it.

"If you're ready to stand by all that you say here, Jimmy," she said finally, "then go ahead—and I'm with you all the way."

I read the letter again, critically this time. There was nothing in it I wanted to change. "I still want to send it."

"Then so do I," she said.

Our nearest post-box was at Bradley's, and on the way there I could see that people knew about the tragedy. They would have heard about it from the policeman's wife, or the vet's children, or some of them might even have seen their vicar, hatless and almost slipperless, flying down the path like a lunatic.

Here and there small knots of people stood talking. There were smiles and acknowledgments as I passed and, as far as one could judge, the memory of the newspaper report had been erased. The church-going villagers had accepted me and seemed pleased with what the church was trying to do. They, I was sure, would realise that my letter to the *County Times* was the only way of reaching those who did not attend the church.

As I dropped the letter into the box, I wondered if the editor would use it. Not that it really affected the position. I had delivered my soul of what I felt was right. Whether the letter ever saw the light of day or not was beyond my power to arrange.

Margaret was getting lunch when I arrived back. She was being harassed by Robert and Susan, who were pushing and pulling at each other around and between her legs. Seeing me, she mouthed through the steam of the saucepan "Better-get-it-over-now," nodding at Robert and saying to him, "Go and play with Daddy, Robert." Realising what was expected of me, I took Robert's hand. A flood of depression swept over me.

In the study, I lifted him on to my knee. "Would you like to play with my stapling machine?" I asked, handing him the re-assembled entity. He looked at me suspiciously. Apparently he still remembered the last warning. *Fathers* are an odd lot he seemed to be thinking. *You never know where you are with them.*

For a while we clipped pieces of paper together and then I said as casually as I could, "The swans, Robert..." His face brightened up and rage flared inside me at the thought of what had been done. "Something's happened to them," I continued softly.

He swivelled round to look me full in the face and said straight away, out of long habit, "Norty boys."

I held him a little closer and found the telling easier than I had imagined. It is often like that with children. You wonder how to explain the death of a relative and then find that they accept it all with a simple and touching faith that too many adults find impossible to attain. He was still a baby, though—only five —and his imagination was just beginning to work. His lower lip trembled uncontrollably.

Then I had an inspiration. If only such moments came more frequently! "Robert," I said confidingly, "I would like you to do something for me, please." He gazed back at me, this new train of thought dragging his mind from the tragedy itself. "Don't tell Susan about this, will you? She's only a baby and she wouldn't understand like you do. You're a big boy." With the corner of my handkerchief I gently wiped a couple of tears from his cheeks. "You didn't even cry, did you? You're very brave, you know. But will you do that for me? Don't tell Susan just yet."

It cheered him, I could see that, to be given such responsibility. But he was still unable to control his voice, so he nodded desperately, working his head vigorously up and down. Then he slid from my knee and scampered on sturdy legs through the open door and to his mother.

Remaining in the study a little longer, I sat alone with my thoughts; but there were no regrets about having posted the letter. Useless thinking about it, really. None of us could ever do more than wait and see what the morrow brought.

Whatever I expected the morrow to bring, it certainly wasn't a telephone call from David. It came quite early, shortly after I'd finished shaving, and I made no attempt to conceal my surprise and delight. He was so far removed from present problems that the mere sound of his voice was a relief and a balm. The purpose of the call was to inform me that he was on a short touring holiday and planned to descend on us that very afternoon.

"If it wouldn't throw you into a complete flat-spin," he said, "we'd like to stay for a couple of days. Only if it's all right with Margaret, of course. But we wouldn't entail any extra work. Quite self-sufficient and all that."

" 'We', David?"

"Oh, I thought I'd mentioned it. I'd like to bring Amanda." His chuckle sounded hollowly in the earpiece. "Perfectly respectable—separate rooms, own hot and cold, toothbrushes, etc."

It was just like David. You would hear nothing of him for a year or more, then he'd breeze in as if it were only yesterday, taking up the threads of his conversation where last he'd left them, revitalising you with his own boundless energy.

Margaret and I spent the morning preparing rooms for David and Amanda, glad to have something to do. A gloom had settled on the vicarage. The swans had been a topic of conversation between us and the children ever since we'd come to St. Hilda's. To have them struck down in this way was rather like hearing that one of your relatives has been murdered.

We had our eleven o'clock coffee together on the crazy paving outside the drawing-room window. The sun was warm and a softness lay across the glebe. We might almost have been on holiday ourselves, and for some reason I found myself thinking about Major Icely's philosophy of life. We had all the requirements—our own home in the country, some land, books . . . but above all we had what he lacked—each other and the children. I would not have changed places with him, or anyone.

When I had drunk my coffee I decided to call in at the vet's to enquire about the swan.

"Could you call in at Bradley's at the same time," asked Margaret, "and buy some sausages for to-night's supper? You'd better get lots of them. You know David's appetite. Do you think they're engaged?"

"The sausages? Hardly."

"Idiot. You know very well who I mean—David and Amanda."

"I haven't the faintest idea, but I hope so. I like Amanda."

"I'd need to know her better before I was sure," Margaret pondered. "Still, David knows what he's up to. He should know by now the kind of girl who'd make a good wife."

"A grand theory, Margaret, but men don't actually stop to think of whether a girl will make a good wife. Physical attraction seems to outweigh all other considerations. In any event, I don't think David's the marrying kind."

I spoke from experience. When we had married, I'd never dreamt what a wonderful wife Margaret would make. I'd only known that I loved her and wanted to share my life with her. Conscientious almost to a fault, she had made herself ill through overwork—involving herself wholeheartedly in my problems as well as giving the children every care and attention. And despite this she remained physically attractive. There was no fear that she would ever turn herself into the popular conception, or misconception, of what a vicar's wife should be—dull, dowdy and colourless. On the contrary, she took a lively interest in fashion trends and was not a bit ashamed of her pretty face or trim figure.

"I'll bet you're thinking of Babs!" said Margaret accusingly, her voice jerking me from my thoughts. Babs, a very attractive girl, was the daughter of my landlady in the days when I'd first become a curate. Margaret often teased me about her. I shook my head. "I know that look on your face, Jimmy. You were thinking of some pretty girl. Come on, now—which one?"

"I think I'll get the sausages," I replied, making for the drive.

The vet was out when I called but his wife, Mrs. Strickle, answered the door. Her hair was in curlers and she wore a vividly coloured housecoat, but this didn't seem to embarrass her. Without any hesitation, she begged me to come in and see the swan for myself.

I followed her down a long corridor on either side of which were oblong cages. From some of these, muzzles and cautious paws were poked as we passed. Mrs. Strickle threw a word or two to each of the occupants until we arrived on a stone veranda which overlooked the backyards of many shops. Here there were larger cages, in one of which the swan reclined on some straw.

"All her babies have died," Mrs. Strickle informed me, shaking her head sadly.

"Will she recover?"

Instead of addressing me, Mrs. Strickle turned to the swan. "Will she recover, now? Will she? She's very sad about the loss of her family, isn't she? Nothing less than sorrow of heart, isn't it? She neither eats nor drinks, and her vicar has come to inquire after her but she takes no more notice of him than if he were— if he were . . ." She waved a hand behind her, saying, "Give me a word. Quick."

"A curate," I supplied, since she seemed keen on the idea. "I don't like the look of that bird," I added. "It puts me in mind of an invalid I once knew who——"

Mrs. Strickle, agitated, cut me short. "Please—*please!* Not in front of you-know-who. Animals understand much more—much, much more than we realise." She turned back to the swan, opening a little door in the cage and pushing a bowl of gruel towards the listless creature. "Shall we see all that finished up by the time we come back?" she asked. "Shall we?"

We were half-way along the corridor on our way back when Mrs. Strickle suddenly stopped and turned to face me. "What was it you were going to say when I stopped you speaking in front of the swan? Something about an invalid."

"Oh . . . I was going to say that the swan reminded me of a woman I once visited when I was chaplain in a London hospital. She was going to have a leg amputated. Her spirits were very high and she seemed most philosophical about it. But when I went to see her after the operation, something seemed to have gone out of her—the spirit, the will . . . I could see it in her eyes more than anything. It was very disturbing. And the swan has that same look."

"Then it was a mercy I stopped you!" Mrs. Strickle gasped. "It would have upset her, I know. It would have upset her dreadfully." She looked round quickly, as if to make sure that none of the other caged animals had overheard us, and then hurried me to the door.

There were a number of people in Bradley's and I might have had to wait quite a time for my sausages but for the intervention of Major Icely. He was over by the counter placing an order. Spotting me, he asked Mrs. Bradley to serve me right away as he wanted to carry me off for a chat. In a London store such action might have provoked a lynching, but here it didn't seem to matter. No one objected.

Despite my protestations, Icely insisted that we have a spot of lunch together.

"But the sausages!" I said weakly as he marched me into the cosy little restaurant called The Lantern. "And Margaret. She'll wonder where on earth I've got to."

"That's soon taken care of. Good day, Mrs. Tamplin"—this to the proprietress as she came out to greet us—"may I use your telephone, please?" A moment or two later he was chaffing Margaret in his clipped voice. "Ah, the vicar's lady! No prizes offered for guessing who this is. I just caught your husband in the village. Poor chap looked half-starved so I'm going to feed him up a bit before sending him home . . . Eh? . . . No, I don't!" It was clear from his laughter that Margaret was playing up to him. "What's that? . . . Ha! Sausages, indeed!" Margaret was, by now, quite used to his habit of telephoning. He did it quite often on the slightest pretext. Actually, I think he loved the 'phone. Living by himself, I suppose it provided him with a certain amount of companionship, albeit remote.

Over soup we discussed the swan episode, Icely taking the line that the village should form a vigilantes group. "No one bothers to make a really strong protest at the damage continually being done by the young," he said.

"Well, I have," I told him. "I've just posted a letter to the *County Times* about it. Whether or not it is printed remains to be seen."

"Oh——" he began, but at that moment the restaurant door bell clanged and he ducked suddenly behind the menu. I looked round to see Mrs. Pankhurst entering. She was wearing a leather coat, tweed skirt, and dark green stockings. Over her arm she carried one of those baskets people use when weeding their gardens. Behind her, as she made her way to the counter, her two dogs set to work giving the tables and chairs a thorough sniffing. Turning to call them, she caught sight of us and immediately crossed to our table.

"Don't get up," she said as we started to rise. "I can't stop for more than a moment."

Although never at a loss for words when I visited her, it was amazing to see her now with Icely—scarcely daring to raise her eyes to his and addressing most of her remarks to me. When he spoke to her, calling her Norah, she still kept her eyes on me though replying to him. She, I noticed, addressed him as "Major". I felt rather uncomfortable sitting there while she stood, particularly as her "moment" stretched into quite a few minutes.

When she had gone, with cries of "Here, Budsy. Come, Scamper!", I said to Icely, "I think she's rather fond of you."

"My dear Jim," he replied, "the village talks of nothing else. Norah is a delightful person and she's very astute, but whenever she talks about me she gives herself away. I've known her a very long time."

I didn't like to comment, but he supplied the answer himself. "A very suitable match, wouldn't you say? She comes from a first-class family—loaded with cash, even though you might not think it. Mind you, she doesn't spend it extravagantly. She's intelligent—but you must have realised that already."

"I visit her quite a bit."

"Which shows your good sense. But I expect, in view of what I've just said, you're wondering why we don't make a match of it . . ." He hesitated, looking out of the window as if wondering whether to continue. Following his gaze, I saw Bresewell in his pony and trap going down the street. Icely had noticed him too. Perhaps it was the sight of the pork-pie hat that gave him confidence. "When you marry, Jim, it has to be for more than class or money or brain. It's . . ."

"Love?"

"In a way—but more so. It involves sleeping with someone. I think I can say that although I could find it in my heart to love Norah I could never sleep with her. It puts me in mind of a passage in the Bible——" He broke off to interject, "If I didn't know you well enough by now I wouldn't be saying these things . . . It's that part where King David is old and it says 'he gat no heat'. They brought him young virgins that they might bring warmth to his tired blood." His eyes twinkled. "I often wonder when that old——what Bresewell makes of that particular scripture." He sighed. "I long to marry, Jim, but marriage has passed me by. Even if a miracle happened and someone could be found to love me, I'd still need to love her with the body as well as the mind."

"I know what you mean," I said, recalling my own thoughts of the morning, my completeness underlining his loneliness.

"I suppose you might say I have a young outlook." He was gazing down at his empty plate. "I need to marry someone young. At my age that's virtually an impossibility."

Although inclined to agree with him, it seemed impolite to say so. "You never know," I said. "Something may turn up."

After the meal we strolled through the village, Icely leaving me just before we reached the vicarage. The more I saw of him, the more it seemed that we had similar points of view and interests. In many ways he was like David—and now the thought of David's arrival caused me to hurry my footsteps. As I turned into the drive I saw the familiar car outside the front door. And David, swathed in a cassock, came from the house to meet me.

"Jim! How marvellous!" He was shaking me affectionately by the shoulders. "We are united once again. This is wonderful."

"It's good to see you after so long," I said.

"Not just me. Amanda's here, you know." His eyes twinkled. "Amanda! Amanda, darling! Come and greet mine host."

She came, slender and supple, from the dining-room looking like a blonde and beautiful picture of "What every Vicarage Needs".

"Kiss him, Amanda," David urged. "Go on. He won't bite. Give him a kiss."

Powerless to prevent her, and feeling rather foolish, I just stood there as she raised her arms like a child and slid them round my neck. A pair of moist and glistening lips narrowly missed my mouth. It was a disturbing sensation and I may have blushed, for David roared his approval.

"Splendid, splendid! Why, here's Margaret. Come here, Margaret. I'm going to kiss you, just to make the score one-all." He enveloped her in his great arms, and when she reappeared he stood back appraising her. "Like it?"

"If you mean being plunged face first into a gooseberry bush," Margaret said, "I'm not quite sure. Why don't you shave the thing off?"

"Never! Absolutely never. What about the egg without salt and all that? It wouldn't be me without the beard."

Indoors, and after the small talk, I told them about the swan.

"Jim's written to the local paper about it," Margaret said, and Amanda gazed at me with enormous eyes as if I'd performed some deed of daring.

"I can't tell you how I feel about this, Jim," David commented. "It must have been absolutely beastly for you both. However, Amanda and I are going to take you all out for a day by the sea or to some other part of the countryside to-morrow. Otherwise you'll all go on brooding about this dreadful thing. Well—what do you say? Don't tell me you've got a funeral or a wedding or something lined up for to-morrow..."

We woke to a crisp bright morning, one with the promise of long hours of sunshine, and I was early in the kitchen in order to have breakfast done before Margaret was up. But David had beaten me to it. Dressed in his cassock, he was frying bacon, peeling the rashers from an enormous pile on the table.

"Delicious smell, Jim, isn't it?" he greeted me. "I'm doing two for each of us—and it's all my own bacon. I've a little refrigerated larder in the boot of the car and I'm absolutely determined that you and Margaret are not going to be out of pocket over our stay."

"You mustn't do that, David," I protested. "You're our guests
... there are lots of eggs and things."

"You provide the bed, I'll provide the board. Now then, what's
it going to be to-day—sea or country? The choice is yours."

"The children would like the sea."

"Of course they would! I wasn't thinking. The sea it is."

"Will you wear your cassock?"

He crouched back in mock alarm, holding up the bacon slice
as if to ward off an attack. "It's the uniform of the church, isn't
it? I might possibly remove it for a swim, though."

Like many bachelors who take a pride in being able to do
things for themselves and even enjoy it, David would permit no
aid. All I had to do was to keep out of his way and listen to
his running commentary.

In the midst of this, Margaret suddenly appeared in her
dressing gown. "Heavens, David, you're up!" she exclaimed,
starting to retreat. "I'll go and change."

He stopped her in the doorway. "You look absolutely charming
just as you are. Have breakfast like that. Amanda will no doubt
appear practically naked, so it will help to redress the balance."

With Amanda came the children, each holding one of her
hands, and David's forecast was not far wrong. She was wearing
an abbreviated mandarin-style beach jacket with the shortest pair
of shorts I've ever seen. The overall effect was that of having
breakfast with a pantomime principal "boy" who hadn't had
time to change her costume.

"They're darlings, David," she said, referring to our offspring.
"These little people have been in my bed since about five o'clock
or some such ghastly hour. When I woke up it was still dark
and something soft was lying across my face—a hand! I was
petrified. A haunted rectory!"

"Vicarage, darling," corrected David.

"Vicarage, then. Before I could scream for help, I recognised
it to be a small person so I let him climb into my bed. Then, a
little later, another small person appeared and she climbed into
my bed too!"

Robert, who had been looking up at Amanda drinking in her

every word, now beamed on us all. "And she doesn't wear any pyjamas, Daddy," he said.

That Thursday, I suppose, was the last completely happy day Margaret and I were to have for some little while and perhaps we sensed it. In any event, we certainly made the most of it. The four of us romped and played with the children on the warm sand as if we were children ourselves. David, still in his cassock, would hurl himself at Margaret in her two-piece swimsuit, or me in my trunks, or Amanda in her bikini, in a desperate attempt to get hold of the beach ball and was, of course, the cynosure of all eyes. Some of the onlookers must have revised any ideas they'd had of the stuffiness of the church.

Lunch was nothing less than a feast. From the car David and Amanda carried a packed hamper containing cold chicken, salad, oysters, French bread, Gruyère cheese and wine, complete with cutlery, napkins and tumblers. I couldn't think when they'd had time to prepare it, but I didn't ask any questions. It was all part of the magic of the day.

We sat in a circle to eat, the children huddling close to Amanda and vying to feed her with potato crisps. They had obviously adopted her.

"I can't thank you enough for this, David," said Margaret. "Robert's been so down in the dumps. This is the first time I've seen him really enjoying himself since the swan business."

"Don't mention it," David replied. "I'm having fun too, aren't I? Incidentally, Jim . . ." He called across to me. "What about that letter you sent to the paper? When can we see it?"

"I've a copy at home, if that's what you mean. I don't know if the paper will print it."

"When does it come out?"

"Friday."

"It's delivered to us on Friday," Margaret put in, "but you can get it in the town on Thursday evening. If we go home that way we might be able to pick up a copy."

The rest of the day passed all too quickly. After lunch we had a siesta, even Robert and Susan seeming content to remain quiet. Then there were more games, and the children had to paddle for a while, yelling with delight as the cold water lapped over their ankles. But at last it was time to think of returning home.

Reluctantly we packed the things into the car and settled down for the journey, Susan on Amanda's lap in the front and Robert between Margaret and me on the back seat. There'd been a bit of a tussle about that but we'd been able to make Robert see that it would be silly for a big boy to sit on someone's lap when he could have a seat of his own.

I must have dozed in the comfort of the car, for I didn't know we had reached County Town until Margaret shook my arm. "The paper, Jim. What about the paper? They sell it on the stands."

David must have been thinking of it too. Before I could call out to him, he had pulled in at the kerb opposite a news-stand. "The *Times*," he called to the vendor, proffering a coin and receiving the paper with the same hand. "You'd better look, Margaret," he said, passing the paper to her over his shoulder. "Jim's half asleep."

"*Completely* asleep!" Margaret amended, starting to scour the pages as the car shot off again on the last lap of the journey.

"It's beginning to get dark," I mumbled drowsily to prove that I knew what was going on around me. "You'll strain your eyes. Wait till we get home."

Robert was asleep, his head pressing against my arm, and I closed my eyes again contentedly, not thinking of anything in particular. Perhaps I dozed again.

"It's here!" Margaret's voice jerked me back from a nether-land of nothingness with a suddenness that made my heart thump. "You'd hardly notice it," she went on, "but it's here." Passing the folded paper across Robert's recumbent form, she pointed towards the bottom of the page.

My letter was there in its entirety. It was in small type beneath a discreet heading: "Vicar of St. Hilda's Concerned about Discipline of Children". I looked at it without really reading it, not knowing whether I felt relief or disappointment that they had not made more of it.

★ 8 ★

BILL TOMLINSON called the next morning, rather to my surprise. Since his initial Friday visit he had made it a habit to call at the beginning of the week. He'd had all my news items on the Monday. Nevertheless I was glad to see him and took him into the study, where we talked about the church, his exams, and the weather before he got around to the point of his visit.

"You know I don't usually come on Fridays, sir, but to-day I felt I had to. It's that letter of yours about the swans. I wanted you to know how much I like it."

"That's very nice of you. Thanks."

"Well, that's not all, sir. I think our editor should have given it more space and what I wanted to do was ask you if I could have your permission to send a copy of it to the nationals."

"To the London papers? They wouldn't be interested, surely!"

"I think they would, sir. After all, it's really a national problem but people only seem to take notice when an isolated case is brought to their attention."

I couldn't help smiling. "It seems as though your mother's ambitions for you are not so far wrong. You appear to have a nose for news!"

He grinned. "Yes...well, may I, sir? I wouldn't quote you. I'd just send the letter as it stands."

"It wouldn't matter if you did quote me. I'm quite prepared to stand by what I say. As a matter of fact, you don't need my permission. The moment I posted the letter it ceased to be my property. It belongs to your paper and I suppose you can do what you like with it."

"I suppose so, sir; but I didn't want to do anything without your permission. Not after the trouble you had with that 'pagan' speech."

"Well," I said appreciatively, "I wouldn't dream of saying no."

"Then I may send it in?"

"If you really want to. I'd like to think it would be used. And it's quite different from the other thing. I'm more careful now and I only say exactly what I mean."

Thanking me, Tomlinson made it clear that he wanted to dash off without wasting any more time and get copies sent away. On our way to the door we caught a glimpse of David entering the dining-room. I saw Tomlinson gape at the bearded, cassocked figure and hesitate. He was obviously torn between the desire to ask questions and the urgency of despatching my letter. The letter won—but I couldn't help wondering what would have happened if Amanda had appeared too.

David was delighted with Tomlinson's proposal when I told him about it.

"Excellent idea," he said. "A vicar's always good for a little publicity. It might take a week or two, but I bet one of the Sunday papers takes it up. You'll see."

In fact, when David and Amanda had said their good-byes on the Saturday afternoon and were sitting in the car ready to drive out of our lives once again, David's final cry was "See you in the Sunday papers!"

That he was right goes without saying, but that it should have been so soon must have surprised him as much as it did me. When I came out of church on Sunday morning after the eight o'clock service, Mrs. Charmian was waiting for me.

"Have you seen them?" she asked excitedly. "They're simply full of you."

"Who?" I asked in bewilderment.

"Then you haven't! And it's not 'who'. It's the Sunday papers. There was something in ours about you and the swans so I ran over to Mrs. Bradley and she let me have copies of the others. It's in nearly all of them!"

"Really?" I said. "That's quick work. It looks as though some-one has a conscience."

"You must come and see them. Some of them even have pictures."

She almost ran me to her house, through the hall and into the parlour overlooking the river. The papers were spread over the table, sofa and chairs and her husband was studying them. I didn't often see Mr. Charmian. Though a delightful man he was not really a churchgoer and tended to avoid me as much as possible. This was obviously a special occasion. And I soon saw why.

I'd imagined that Mrs. Charmian had found the paragraphs tucked away in the heart of various newspapers, but it wasn't like that at all. The story, to my amazement, had been given considerable prominence. One of the more serious newspapers had headed the item "Vicar asks 'When will we discipline our children?' ", following it with a couple of inches of type at the foot of which it said in italics *See Editorial*.

In the tabloids there was less restraint, each seeming determined to outdo the other. Great banner headlines snaked in and out among pictures of buxom bathing beauties: VICAR GRIEVES OVER SWANS — VICAR LASHES OUT AT ST. HILDA'S "SAVAGES", ASKS "WHEN?" — MINISTER HITS OUT AT HOOLIGANS. Even without having heard of St. Hilda's, one could scarcely fail to be interested. One paper carried a photo of the nest with a large magnifying glass superimposed above. This drew attention to a brick lying near by.

"Could I borrow some of these, Mrs. Charmian?" I asked. "I'd like to show them to Margaret."

"Do, Vicar, please do. Isn't it dreadful?"

"Dreadful? It should do a lot of good."

"I mean, it's just what people may say and how they'll take it in the village." She hesitated for a moment and then picked up one of the papers. "Did you see this bit?" She pointed to the end of a column. I took the paper and read:

Mrs. Quimbolt, one of St. Hilda's oldest residents, had this to say when I called upon her in her cottage behind the Norman church. "My husband has been verger of St. Hilda's for forty years. We work hard for the church but that doesn't mean we agree with everything the vicar says. The children of our village are as good as any in the country, I say. They have their little ways, but what child hasn't? What I'd like to know is why the vicar writes like this about St. Hilda's children. He knows how hard it is to look after them. Why, only a few weeks ago his own child was lost!"

"But that's ridiculous," I said, giving her back the paper. "The two things are totally different. In one case you get a little boy running off. In the other you get this senseless, brutal slaughter."

"I know, Vicar, but I'll never forgive myself for losing Robert. It's the very thing people will pick on when they read all this. It's what they will say."

"It doesn't matter what they say, Mrs. Charmian. What really matters is whether or not a thing is true. And it is true that the swans were wantonly destroyed."

"Ah, well!" Mr. Charmian said cheerfully. "There's nothing like getting your name into the papers for causing a bit of excitement."

"If it helps to stir people out of their lethargy," I replied as Mrs. Charmian folded the newspapers for me to take back to the vicarage, "it'll be worth it."

Margaret's reaction to the publicity was mixed. She was impressed but also slightly perturbed.

"This is a bit more than we bargained for, isn't it?" she said, scanning the various reports. "They couldn't have received the letter until Saturday—yet look at the lengths they've gone to—interviews, photographs . . . I wonder why . . . ?"

"Because it seems to have coincided with a number of outbreaks of violence in the London area—young thugs attacking girls and old people. Look at some of the stories in smaller print that follow our piece. I suppose they felt that a cry from further afield might highlight local problems. Or perhaps they were glad to be able to show that this is not only a 'big city' problem. I don't know."

"And how do you think the villagers will take it?"

"I don't know that, either. But I know how they *should* take it. The guilty should be conscience-stricken and the rest should

be glad that something is being done to put a stop to such out-
rages."

"Of course!" said Margaret, brightening. "I am an idiot. Why
didn't I think of that?"

On Tuesday, however, when Margaret came in from doing
some shopping she was unusually silent. I found her in the
kitchen, hat and coat still on, shopping basket still loaded, staring
through the window.

"Looking for something?" I asked jovially.

She turned to face me, serious and troubled. "I've just been
cut dead two or three times in the High Street—Mrs. Sancroft,
Miss Lefevre . . . some others who usually smile and nod. They
all suddenly found things of vital interest to capture their attention in shop windows or on hoardings as I passed. Miss Lefevre
didn't even bother to camouflage. She just looked through me."

"You're not just imagining it?"

"Of course not, Jimmy. They saw me. I'm sure of it."

"Then you think it's because of . . ."

"The letter? What else?"

"But it doesn't make sense. Why Miss Lefevre? If anyone
was going to take offence, it should be the parent of a guilty
child."

"Unfortunately, it seems that their minds don't work like
ours."

"It's just ridiculous. What's the matter with them? Don't
they care about the swans?"

Margaret dragged off her hat and threw it on to a small table.
"I don't know. All I know is that people who talked to me last
week looked right through me this morning. What am I supposed to do?"

"Put out your tongue at them," I suggested lightly, in an
attempt to bring a smile to her face. But she was not to be
jollied out of this.

"Don't be silly, Jim. We have to live here. We are supposed
to be nice and gentle and kind and loving."

"And I hope we are. I was only joking. We've been cut
before, though. Remember Mrs. Parlett in the last parish?"

"Yes . . . I'm sorry, darling, for going off like this. I suppose it will wear off . . . but if only people knew what it was really like to be a parson or a parson's wife. I don't enjoy being cut."

"Nor do I. But if it's a choice between that and the freedom to say what I think and know to be true, I know which I'd rather have."

She smiled now. "I *do* like you, you know. You're good for me. And I won't weaken. We'll just have to dig in our heels and get set for a rather trying time."

Margaret was right. The next few days were sticky. There were many in the village who were annoyed at the press reports but didn't like to say so openly. As far as I could ascertain, the people who had been upset by my first unguarded remarks about pagans were the same people who now took offence. It was impossible to walk through the village without meeting some of them and it was equally impossible to be unaware of their silent hostility. I could only grit my teeth and carry on, believing that those who objected would eventually forget their grievances.

Thursday morning brought the first of several admonitory letters I was to receive. It came from a lady whose acquaintance I had yet to make, in fact I had not known of her existence. I learned later that she was a middle-aged widow living a solitary existence in a cottage a mile and a half outside the village. She had never attended church since my arrival and I had not yet got around to calling on her as had been my intention. Thus we had never met, but this did not discourage my correspondent.

The tone of the letter was severe. It warned me to be under no misapprehension concerning the intense anger my letter to the newspaper editor had aroused in the village. It pointed out— what I had never denied—that the behaviour of most of the local children was exemplary, and that to condemn them all because of the thoughtless action of one, or perhaps two, of them was lamentably lacking in the Christian charity of which I, an ordained minister of God, should have exhibited to the utmost.

Apart from the fact that she had read a meaning into my letter which was never intended, indeed was never there, I thought her own description of the wanton slaughtering of the swans as a "thoughtless action" the understatement of all time. The whole letter was quite ludicrous, and deserved no more than to be tossed into the waste-paper basket. Yet I could not do it. Instead I read it again, and then a third time. And each time I read it, my blood boiled a little more.

What right had this woman who was not even a member of my congregation to censure my actions and lecture me on Christian charity? Quite obviously she was a crank, a busybody who had got all her facts wrong. But had she? At least the bit in her letter in which she said I had stirred up anger in the village was true enough. Margaret had already discovered this to her cost, poor dear.

Sorely troubled, my first impulse was to find Margaret and show her the letter, deriving compensation from the anger I knew she would feel. But when I found her she was in the kitchen mixing a cake and I didn't have the heart to trouble her.

The rest of the day was busy. I had a sermon to finish, some writing to do, and my English class in County Town—which turned out to be more than usually ghastly. And try as I might, I could not get that letter out of my mind.

In the evening we had our prayer meeting. It took place every Monday and was never very well attended. We would have a hymn, a passage of scripture expounded by me, a short discussion, and then extempore prayer. The people who came were, with one or two exceptions, too shy to enter very heartily into the discussion or lead the rest of us in prayer, so it was never an easy meeting. Sometimes one or two of them would stop to have a chat with me and help to collect the books, but on this occasion no one did and I collected the books myself. These I shot into the green cupboard which stood beneath the picture of Daniel in the Lions' Den. Then I snapped down the mains switch in the black iron box and, feeling for my bunch of keys, stepped through the curtains hanging over the door and out into the street.

On the way home a black Rolls-Royce drew up at the curb

alongside me. Charrington-Hawes was driving. He put his head out of the window.

"Could you spare me a few minutes, Vicar?" he asked.

"Certainly," I replied, and climbed in beside him.

We set off and I settled into the deep upholstery with appreciation. Wonderful to have a car like this, I thought.

"I thought we might look in on Jeremiah," Charrington-Hawes said. "I think we ought to discuss this business as soon as possible."

"What business?" I asked, and I felt suddenly uneasy, almost guilty.

"This letter you wrote to the press," he replied evenly. "It's given rise to a good deal of concern in the village, and I can't say I'm altogether surprised."

"But that's ridiculous," I protested.

"Is it? Well, let's wait till we reach Jones' place till we discuss it."

We lapsed into silence while the big car smoothly purred the short distance to the farmhouse. Three minutes later we were seated in Jeremiah's low-ceilinged parlour, all three of us feeling anything but comfortable. Charrington-Hawes came straight to the point.

"I've just told the vicar, Jeremiah, that the people round here deprecate the tone and content of his letter to the *County Times*."

"Yes, indeed," Jones agreed, nodding his head.

"Both Jones and I," Charrington-Hawes went on, "have received a number of telephone calls complaining about it."

"I can't think why."

"Oh, come, Vicar, that's unworthy of you. Surely you must expect people to object if you take it upon yourself to rush into print with an attack on the children of this village."

"But I haven't attacked the children of this village or, at least, only those who were guilty of a dreadful action. And they deserve far worse than I can give them."

"I readily believe that that was your intention. Unfortunately, however, you did not make it evident in your letter. I think people are entitled to believe you have held up the children of St. Hilda's before the whole nation as irresponsible hooligans."

"Oh no, Mr. Harrington-Chawes," I said, stumbling over his name in the agitation I was trying to control. "I think you are being most unfair. My letter did not give the impression you ascribe to it. It was perfectly straightforward."

"Well, that is how it read to us," he said implacably.

"Then you could not have read it correctly. I was most careful that there should be no other interpretation."

I suddenly realised with a shock that I was raising my voice in anger and frustration. Whatever happens I mustn't lose my temper, I thought. Yet was ever a man more sorely tried! Charrington-Hawes spoke again; by comparison his quiet, precise voice made it sound as though I had been shouting from the house-tops.

"I'm sorry you don't see this matter as we do, Vicar. Very sorry, indeed. I had hoped that this little chat this evening might have saved things from going further."

"What do you mean, 'going further'?"

"I dislike intensely having to say this, Vicar, but there is a vociferous element in the village that is demanding either a public apology from you, or that a meeting be called to enable them officially to register their disapproval. I hope you won't think it disloyal in me when I say that I share their views."

"It's a serious matter," said Jones, speaking for the first time.

"Serious!" I echoed. "It's tantamount to a declaration of lack of confidence in me. If you gentlemen call this meeting you will obviously not be able to continue to act as my wardens."

"We will cross that bridge when we come to it," said Charrington-Hawes. "Meanwhile, I must reserve to myself the right to act according to my conscience. I am quite sure you would not wish to deny me that, Vicar."

"I would deny you nothing, but I had thought to find a greater measure of understanding in you."

"Understanding? The only thing that surpasses my understanding is why you wrote so foolish a letter."

"I wrote it because I wanted to," I replied with slow deliberation. "Because I felt I had to. Because it was the only way of reaching the people of the village who don't come to church. Because I don't approve of swans being battered to death. I can give you a dozen equally good reasons if you want them."

"All right, that much I accept. But why must you impugn every child in the parish?"

At this I closed my eyes and offered up a silent prayer for patience and forbearance. "I—did—not—impugn—every—child —in—the—parish," I said, clinging to the last vestiges of my sanity.

"You did. You called them savages." I thought for one dreadful moment he was going to add: "as you once called their parents pagans." Instead, he said with genuine sorrow in his voice. "You know, Vicar, you do put your pen to the most unfortunate uses."

"If you are referring to the earlier newspaper incident," I said bitterly, "it was a report of the spoken word. I did not write it. I did write this letter, however, and I knew exactly what I was writing—and I do not withdraw one word of it."

"Then, I am afraid nothing further is to be gained by our remaining here. I'll run you back to the vicarage, Vicar."

"Thank you, but please don't take it amiss if I refuse." I laughed nervously. "I'm desperately in need of a walk as you can probably guess. But before I go, just let me say this. Mr. Charrington-Hawes has spoken of acting according to his conscience, and that is precisely what I am doing at this moment. I have taken my stand by what I sincerely believe to be right. No more can be expected of any man." Speaking these words I was suddenly oppressed by their extreme pomposity, but it was too late to do anything about it. I shook hands with Charrington-Hawes and Jones accompanied me to the front door.

"I'm deeply sorry about this rift, Vicar," he said. "We must all work and pray that it will be soon bridged."

"I'll say 'Amen' to that," I replied, and stalked off into the darkness.

When I reached the vicarage, the hall was in darkness and Margaret was in bed. Needing time to calm myself before facing her, I went into the kitchen and put some milk to warm on the stove. My hands were shaking as I held the saucepan.

In a while I began to relax, even to smile at the absurdity of it all. How ridiculous we must have looked—Charrington-Hawes, Jones and myself—mouthing words at each other, bristling and barking.

I took Margaret a cup of cocoa and sat on the bed, still smiling. "You should have seen us," I said. "Like three children, making faces at each other." I began to tell her the whole story and, as it unfolded, all amusement went. There was nothing funny about it. Where I should have been patient and gentle and understanding, I had been irritable and angry—a victim of the very emotions I was supposed to subdue in others. It might have been excusable if my two wardens had been brash, provocative men. But they weren't. They were genuinely saddened by the turn of events and would have gladly rallied to my side had they been able to do so. I knew I had deeply disappointed them, but could not bring myself to retract. Filled with self-doubt, I let the story trail to its close. When it was done, Margaret put her hand in mine.

"I know how you feel," she said, "but if that's all that happened then you have nothing to reproach yourself for at all. Honestly, darling. Nothing at all."

My quarrel with the wardens was a miserable business. It was bad enough to have a number of people in the congregation and village against me, but these were men who had voluntarily accepted office in order to support and help me. The situation would have to be resolved as quickly as possible and I wanted to see the rural dean immediately to ask for his advice. When I telephoned the rectory, however, I learned that he was just out of hospital but would be glad to see me once the week-end was over. Unfortunately, this meant facing the wardens again on Sunday without knowing exactly what I could or could not do.

It was normal at St. Hilda's for the vicar's warden and the people's warden to be in and out of the vestry before the service commenced while arranging various matters in the church—

seeing to sidesmen, finding the lessons in the big lectern Bible, greeting newcomers. All of which was usually done in a spirit of camaraderie and friendliness. It was all cheerfully informal, each of us doing his appointed job, and breaking off now and then maybe to exchange some pleasantry or a few words of gossip. Desperately I hoped that this happy atmosphere would persist despite our differences; that outwardly at least we would continue to be the same happy family we had been before.

When I arrived at the church for the eleven o'clock morning service I saw a grey trilby and a light brown cap hanging in the vestry and knew that both the wardens were present. My heart sank a little and I realised that I must have been nourishing a hope that they wouldn't turn up. Slipping into a cassock, I took the banns book and placed it in its usual position in my stall. Across the pews, I saw the two wardens at the back of the church by the font. They had their heads together and seemed to be talking hard.

A few minutes before the service commenced it was customary that the wardens should join the vicar for a short prayer in the vestry, after which I would cross over to collect the choir from the other side of the church. Both men now came in with rather a rush and although they shook hands with me it was done rather stiffly. There was great tension in the room as I said our prayer.

After the service I hurried home, glad that the ordeal was over. It was difficult to know how to handle the situation, but I was convinced that the rural dean would solve the problem once I was able to see him.

Throughout the day I re-lived the conversation of the previous Monday evening, trying to recall every single remark and the way it was made. Not content with that, I went back in my mind to the original incident of the swans' nest, asking myself if I had perhaps been wrong to object as I had done. It still seemed to me that I'd acted correctly. What I couldn't understand was why such a perfectly simple thing should have caused such a furore. Even supposing I had committed the crime of which I was accused, that I had branded all the village children savages, did it warrant such stern measures as my accusers proposed to take? I didn't know. What I did know was that the feeling was widespread and growing, and that I should have to take strong measures to counteract it if I was to continue with my ministry and regain the confidence of my parishioners. And this last was a problem that was never out of my mind for more than a few minutes at a time. What steps were open to a parson in my position? Who had the authority to legislate between him and his congregation? Again I did not know, but I did know that for my own peace of mind some solution for return of harmony would have to be found very soon.

At tea-time, still deep in thought, I was unable to enjoy Robert and Susan's conversation. For once, they were in quiet and companionable mood. At such rare times they were usually at their most amusing, but now it was wasted on me.

"Worrying, darling?" asked Margaret.

"You know how it is," I said, sorry that I was not better at hiding my feelings.

"Try and think of something else—the cottage, for instance."

I smiled. "The cottage" was a dream we had of one day living a quiet private life in a tiny cottage of our own. Since neither of us did the football pools, the only chance of its ever coming true would be through my writing. This made the likelihood pretty remote, but we enjoyed thinking about it.

"You can smile," Margaret went on, "but I think we could have it one day. You don't, do you?"

"What makes you think that?" I asked.

"Because you don't really want it. This is your vocation, and you'd never really want to cut yourself off from your work. You're too fond of people."

"People like Charrington-Hawes and Jones?"

"Yes, them above all others. That's why you're right for this job. It is your vocation."

It was a roundabout way of giving me her vote of confidence, but I was grateful for it. She wasn't going to let us get too emotional about it, though. Lifting Susan from her chair she said, "Go and cheer Daddy up. Show him how much you love him."

The little girl, warm and sticky, plump and round, climbed on to my lap, putting her face close to mine and squeezing me in an access of feeling. I laughed and hugged her to me, at which Robert scrambled from his chair and came hurrying across with a determined look on his face. There seemed little doubt that he meant to clout Susan.

"I'd better get to church, Margaret," I said hurriedly, putting Susan down.

"Well, don't worry," she replied. "Whatever happens, they won't eat you."

It was to be expected that the evening service should see little change in the general situation, that we would be no further on one way or the other. This would have suited me very well because I was now content to leave things until I'd had time to consult the rural dean. But things rarely turn out the way one expects.

Before Evensong commenced I knelt, as I usually did, at the Communion rails for a short prayer. During this the conviction came to me that, if I were a Christian at all, I must now do all in my power to heal the breach between me and my wardens. There could be no waiting for the rural dean. I would have to make the peace myself. Part of me—the part I struggled most desperately to suppress—reacted violently against the idea. They started the trouble, I thought, let them take the consequences. Why should I be conciliatory? But deep in my heart there was no doubt about what I had to do, and I went back into the vestry to await the wardens' arrival. When they appeared I asked if they would mind waiting for a few minutes after the service as I wished to have a word with them. They both looked a bit surprised but agreed to do so.

Throughout the service I kept thinking about what I intended to do. The only Christian course was to apologise for the way in which I had raised my voice and shouted on Monday evening. I would suggest that we shake hands and forget the whole un-fortunate matter so that we might continue to work together for God.

Once having made the decision, I felt much happier. Even so, before the last hymn arrived there were a number of attempts made to get me to change my mind. *What good will it do?* asked the voice inside me. *It will only be interpreted as weakness. Stick to your guns, man. You've nothing to be ashamed of.* A Christian, however, must try to show love wherever he can. If I were to extend the hand of friendship now, how could it be refused?

In the vestry, after the service, the wardens counted the collection while I attended to one person after another who wished to speak to me. This seemed to take longer than usual and Charrington-Hawes and Jones, having finished the collection, stood around awkwardly and fiddled with things on the table. But at last there was no one left to talk to and, feeling very nervous, I shut the door and turned to the two men.

"Sorry to keep you waiting," I said. "Shall we sit down here at the table?"

We sat. I twisted my fingers nervously, working them together, holding my hands before me on the table-cloth, trying to remember the introduction I had planned.

"Mr. Charrington-Hawes, Mr. Jones, I—I wanted to have a word about Monday night. I want—that is, I would like to apologise for the way in which I spoke—raised my voice—in anger. Nothing is ever accomplished by losing one's temper. I regret it very much. I should have discussed the whole matter in a calm and dispassionate way."

There was a short silence and I felt that my words had been well received. For myself, having got the apology off my chest, I felt greatly relieved. In a moment or two, I almost convinced myself, they would suggest there had been faults on both sides, that they had been a little over-hasty and that the best thing was to forget the whole business. As usual, Charrington-Hawes acted as the spokesman.

"That is a handsome apology, Vicar," he said. "Thank you for it. Does it also mean that you have had second thoughts on the matter we discussed. I do pray so."

"I am afraid not. I stand now where I stood before."

"I see." He paused, and then went on, "Then the arrange-
ments for a meeting go on. There can be no other course." `

"You realise that nothing but pain can come of it?"

"But it's nothing personal, Vicar," Jones assured me anxiously.
He looked thoroughly miserable, as though he wished he had no
part in the sorry affair. "It's just that people keep getting on to
us. As recently as this morning someone rang to ask me what
steps we propose to take."

"But you have no authority to call a meeting."

"Anyone who wishes is entitled to call a meeting," Charrington-Hawes reminded me. "And personally I don't think it will
be a bad thing. It will give all those suffering under a sense of
grievance a chance to get it off their chests." There was a finality
in his tone that brooked no further discussion.

"Then naturally," I heard myself saying, "you will not mind
if I take whatever action I choose after consulting the rural
dean."

The three of us rose and made for the door. Before we reached
it, Charrington-Hawes turned to me. "But surely you must
admit, Vicar, that you are in the wrong..."

"In the wrong?"

"You apologised."

"Yes, I did. But only for what happened on Monday evening.
I should have listened calmly to what you both had to say and
answered calmly. With regard to my writing, however, I do not
retract one word."

"Even though it shames our village and our church! In *that*
kind of newspaper and on a Sunday!"

From the way he said "that kind of newspaper" I knew that
he was referring to the juxtaposition of the report about the
St. Hilda's "Savages" and the exciting details that go to make up
a modern tabloid newspaper with its banner headlines and long-
limbed lovelies. His face looked shocked and angry. It was almost
enough to make me laugh aloud at the absurdity of the whole
thing.

Then, suddenly, I saw the whole episode in a possible new
light. Perhaps it was not the fate of the swans that was troubling

the conscience of these good people, nor my strictures on the behaviour of the guilty children, nor even the unfavourable publicity which my letter had brought to the village of St. Hilda's; it was the medium through which the publicity had been expressed that they could not stomach. If it had appeared only in the *County Times*, as I had originally intended, little harm would have been done. But it had gone far beyond this, to the national press and, even more significant, to the *Sunday* press. To the Victorian element among my parishioners that the good name of St. Hilda's should be bandied about by newspapers published on a Sunday, cheek by jowl with details of the latest murder, was tantamount to sacrilege. I looked with new interest at my two wardens. I had never suspected they might hold such views, and even now could scarcely credit it.

But if this was so, surely, my actions were not to be bound by the views of a minority having an outlook more appropriate to the previous century. It was quite absurd, and not to be tolerated in this more enlightened age. Speaking very deliberately I said: "Gentlemen, I realise you owe a duty to the parish as well as to me and I know that neither of you would shrink from either. Nevertheless, I can only repeat what I have already said—that I must be free to say and do what I think is right and best for our community as a whole. I'm sorry to disappoint you, but there it is."

There was nothing more to be said, so we took our leave of each other and went our several ways.

The rural dean lived in a village nine or ten miles distant, to which we were linked by a fairly dependable bus service. It was a pleasant place where ponies, driven from the moors, galloped through the streets until they were finally caught and sold to the public at a low figure.

A pleasant-looking, middle-aged housekeeper opened the door to me and ushered me into the dean's study. There was a neatness about the large room that one didn't often find among those of my calling. Papers were set out tidily on a table and the grate was free of fly-papers and matches. After a few minutes the rural dean, in a wheel-chair, propelled himself into the room. "Hullo, Insight. Glad to see you. Sit yourself down," he said. "I'm afraid I have to stay in this chair for the time being. They took off my leg this time. Don't know what it will be next. There's not much left. Something to do with the blood, you know."

We continued from there to make polite conversation, neither of us apparently anxious to get on to the subject I had come to discuss. I was reminded of a bizarre film I had once seen where a man in a wheel-chair, confronted by a bunch of crooks, had suddenly seized one of them and, holding him as a shield across the chair, shot all the others thus solving all his problems. Such an elementally simple solution would have suited me fine.

"Now," said the rural dean, bringing me back to earth, "what was it you wanted to see me about?"

"I'm in a bit of a fix, sir, and I wondered if you could help me. It's about my wardens."

He offered me a cigarette, which I declined, and I began by telling him how the two wardens had told me the village wanted a meeting to discuss my action in writing to the press.

"Ah, yes," he said, smiling. "Everybody these days wants to have his say. Quite right, too; mustn't have any muzzling of the masses."

"Er, yes, sir. But are they within their rights?"

"Within their rights? Why not? You don't need a licence to call a meeting. They can call a dozen meetings if they like, but of course any decision reached wouldn't be worth the paper it is written on. No official recognition, you see, my boy."

"Yes, sir," I said miserably, "but I do wish they wouldn't go ahead with this one. I asked them not to, but they were adamant."

"Hm! I wonder if I could do something to help."

"If you could, sir, I'd be awfully grateful. I just don't know what to do. I've never handled a situation like this before."

"I'd have to write; I can't get about very well at the moment or I'd go and see them. On second thoughts, it might be better if I have a word with Charrington-Hawes on the 'phone. I was never much of a hand at letter-writing but I flatter myself I can talk," he chuckled. "Heaven knows, I've had enough practice."

"Thank you, sir."

"Now don't go banking too much on it. I can't work miracles but I can tell him you've had this word with me and that I'm on your side. If that doesn't bring home the bacon, I'll tell them I'm sure they would not wish you to undergo further anxiety and will they please call the party off. How's that, polite and to the point. Eh, my boy!"

"Yes, sir," I agreed, doubtfully. "That would be fine, but what shall I do if they go ahead and hold the meeting? I'm absolutely at a loss to know how to handle it. I feel that the village must know a great deal of what has happened already and drawn all manner of conclusions."

There was a tap on the door and a girl came in carrying a tray of tea. I stood up, surprised. She was the redhead I'd seen painting in the churchyard.

"Ah, tea!" said the rural dean. "This is my daughter Irene, Insight." He looked from me to her. "Do you know each other?"

"In a way," she said, putting down the tray.

"We met once outside my church," I supplemented.

She shook my hand firmly, but her eyes were accusing. "You never came to see my studio."

"I know. I've been saving it up. I really do intend to come."

"Irene looks after me most of the time," said the rural dean as she arranged the tea things, "but when she's had enough she escapes to her studio in St. Hilda's." He could not hide his admiration as he spoke of her.

"Leaving him in the capable hands of Mrs. Hodges," added Irene. "She's the woman who let you in. Well—there you are!" She indicated the things on the table. "I'll leave you to it."

When she had gone he poured the tea, telling me that his wife had died some years ago and that Irene was his only child. "She seems to have a passion for painting, you know."

"Yes, sir. I saw a sample of her work the day I met her. It impressed me immensely. She's very good indeed."

"You really think so?"

"I'm no judge, I suppose, but I know what I like. As far as I'm concerned she's quite brilliant."

He beamed. "I've never wanted to tie her down; that's why I suggested a studio in some other village. Do go and visit her when you have time. It would please her, I'm sure."

"I most certainly will."

Reluctant as he was to leave the subject of his daughter, it was he who steered us back to our original topic of conversation.

"Very good. Yes. Well—now, where were we? Ah, yes. The 'phone call. I'll get down to it at once. This talk may help them to come to some understanding with you. You'd feel quite happy to forget the whole thing then and work on with them, wouldn't you?"

"Oh, yes!" Naturally pessimistic, I had been basing all my actions on the assumption that the meeting would be called. Now the rosy vista of working together with the wardens in a new and happier relationship had been opened up.

Irene came in to collect the tea things as I said good-bye to her father. She escorted me to the door.

"The painting of your church is finished, you know. But I'm not going to present it until it's been previewed."

"Jolly good," I said. "The fact is, though, things are rather chaotic at the moment; but I'll come and see it as soon as I possibly can."

"That sounds fair enough," she smiled.

Much encouraged by the morning's interview, I was able to enjoy the ride home along the twisting country road.

The telephone was ringing in the study when I arrived, and Margaret was just emerging from the kitchen.

"I'll take it," I called, dashing in and lifting the receiver.

It was the rural dean, pleased that he'd timed it so well.

"I've had that little chat. All very pleasant and hands-across-the-sea, but I doubt if I got very far. He's a redoubtable character, your Mr. Charrington-Hawes and, what's so remarkable in this post-war world, he knows his own mind. I can only think he must be of my own generation."

"What did he say, sir?"

"Remarkably little, my dear fellow, except that a man has to be guided by his conscience. I said it seemed to me that in this particular instance common-sense might prove the more reliable guide. He said 'yes' but only in certain aspects of it. In other aspects, he could turn only to his conscience. I said that this last lot of aspects were new to me, and he said that that was quite possible. And there the conversation rather bogged down because, quite frankly my boy, I was way out of my depth. What were these other aspects he was talking about?"

"I suspect that they have something to do with Sunday newspapers."

"Sunday newspapers! God bless my soul! Oh well, as I say, I doubt if I have forwarded your cause over-much, but I took the opportunity to give you a good personal build-up. If they hold this meeting, as I'm afraid they intend to do, Charrington-Hawes will be able to inform his friends that you have the support of the Rural Dean in this controversy. Sorry I couldn't do more, my boy. Goodbye-now!"

The line went dead and I replaced the receiver, heaving a massive sigh.

With the rest of the village in such apparent turmoil about the newspaper publicity, it hadn't occurred to me that Mrs. Markesete might also take some interest in the matter. She was now extremely ill, her feverish eyes seeming to glow like hot coals in the pale, thin face.

"Oh, yes," she said, "I know all about it. The Sunday papers are very important to me. They bring the world into this room."

I sat very still, waiting for her to continue, half afraid of what she would have to say. For weeks now we had discussed the possibility of her confirmation, but the decision had not yet been made. I'd never given up hope that she would finally cast aside all her doubts, but now I was not so sure. If the newspaper reports had turned her against me then all the spiritual aid I'd tried to give her would be in vain.

"I've only one thing to say about it, Mr. Insight." She paused, and it was impossible to guess from the expression on her face what the one thing might be.

"Yes?" I encouraged.

"Congratulations."

I let out my breath, which I'd been holding without being aware of it, and said quietly, "Thank you."

"It was about time someone had the courage to do something about the little imps in this village. Knowing the place as I do, I think it was pretty brave of you. What has the reaction been?"

"Not too good, I'm afraid. It's all rather up in the air at the moment—but I'm sure it will work out well in the end."

"You *do* have faith!" She looked down at the coverlet she was bunching in her fingers. "About the other thing—I'll never be strong enough to go to the church, you realise that. How would the bishop feel about coming to a public house? Would he mind?"

"Good heavens, no!" My heart was leaping. "He'd be delighted to come."

She raised her eyes to mine and held my gaze. "In that case, I'd like to be confirmed."

"I'm so glad," I said.

It's been worth it, I thought. If it's helped to bring this about then it's been worth it, no matter what the outcome.

Two days after my visit to the rural dean, a letter arrived by the afternoon post. It was in a large envelope and, guessing what it might contain, I carried it into the study where I'd been just about to sit down to tea, toast and biscuits. The envelope contained a single typewritten sheet of foolscap which was headed "Private and Confidential". There was no address, and the date had been written in ink.

Gently but firmly the statement pointed out that my duties as a parish priest were long and arduous, and they would all feel a lot happier if I would confine my attention to them and resolutely eschew further excursions into letter-writing authorship. The letter concluded on a kiss-and-make-friends note saying how much they had enjoyed working with me in the past few months and how much they looked forward to returning to the same happy relationship in the future.

At the foot of the last page were two columns of signatures, perhaps a score of them in all. One column was headed by Charrington-Hawes and the other by Jones. Against their names were the typewritten words 'Vicar's Warden' and 'People's Warden'. A quick glance at the other names suggested they comprised the entire Standing Committee.

My first reaction was to warm to the essential reasonableness and fairness of the letter. It was, I thought, the letter of kindly Christian men performing an unpleasant duty. Then, when I had read it a second and third time I began to swing to the opposite point of view. I began to see censure where none was merited and the more I thought about it the hotter under the collar I got. It was an impertinence, I caught myself saying aloud, that these people should band together and sit in judgment on my actions. It was laughable that people so narrow in their views, whose whole lives had been confined to this unenlightened neck-of-the-woods, should presume to dictate to me on what I should and should not do. How dare they!

Reading the document a fourth time I came to the conclusion it had been compiled with the thoroughness of an edict from Russia to the Western powers, with a contrived significance behind every word and a hidden barb in every phrase. Looking back I now realise it was its very reasonableness that rankled. They loved their church, they said: Well, so did I. They acknowledged they had no right to criticise, they said. Then, what did they think they were doing writing to me in such terms, I fiercely wanted to know? And when, for Heaven's sake, were they going to get abreast of the times and learn there is nothing darkly evil about a Sunday newspaper, even the less literary ones which cater for popular entertainment?

And look again at that penultimate paragraph! "All of us whose names are appended below are unanimous in the decision taken (are they, indeed!) and hasten to assure you that the matter discussed and the terms of this letter are being treated as strictly confidential." Well, now, isn't that nice of them!

The more I thought about it the more I got worked up and the less rational became my reasoning. Indignation swept over me in waves. My tea and toast were forgotten. It would have choked me to have attempted to eat. That Charrington-Hawes should solemnly collect together a group of people to censure their vicar and set it out in writing like this, no matter how strictly confidential, was a terrible thing. In the Bible, Dathan and Abiram, attempting something similar, found that God took such a serious view of the matter that they and all theirs were swallowed up quickly in a pit of fire.

My first impulse was to rush to the telephone. Then I wanted to grab my pen; and then I wanted to dash straight round to the Charrington-Hawes mansion and confront him. But slowly some sort of sanity returned. Margaret and the children were out, so I could sit back quietly and think. What on earth was I to do? Most certainly I would have to reply—but when, and how? Would it not be best for me to go and see the rural dean once again?

Hearing Margaret's key in the front door, I picked up the letter to slip it in my pocket. It then occurred to me that I had not fully taken in the other names at the bottom. Who actually had attended this meeting? Charrington-Hawes had said it was not official. Jones had declared that there was nothing personal about it. At first glance the names had appeared to include the entire Standing Committee; but now, for the life of me, I couldn't remember exactly who were the members of that committee. There'd be the wardens, of course, the secretary, the treasurer—Sir Henry Triscombe—Bresewell, Saigon . . .

Margaret's head appeared round the study door.

"Hullo, darling. Be with you in a minute."

She vanished, and I heard her hustling the children towards the back of the house.

Hurriedly I searched out an old Church Magazine and discovered the names of the Standing Committee set out from last year's Annual General Meeting and began comparing them with the sheet I'd just received. There was one name at least that I didn't want to find—Icely's. How could I bear it if he had attended the meeting?

Margaret and the youngsters, their faces whipped by the wind, came into the room. Robert and Susan immediately began to tussle at my feet and Margaret bent to kiss me.

"Gosh, you *do* look pale," she said. "You shouldn't be stuck in here on an afternoon like this." She tried to steal a glance at the paper in my hand. "Nothing wrong, is there?" Before I could reply, she prattled on about the walk they'd just had. ". . . and on the way back we ran into Major Icely, didn't we, Robert?"

"Really?" I'd finished scanning the signatures and his name was not there. Thank God for that.

"Jim, you're not listening. Something *is* wrong. What is it?"

"Nothing, Margaret. I'm all right now." I folded the letter and put it in my pocket. "But I'm afraid I won't be in this evening after all. I must go and see the rural dean again."

Just as I closed the vicarage door behind me, a man came hurrying up the drive. It was Rafferty, looking, if anything, a little seedier than usual. He didn't want to keep me long, since it was obvious I was in a hurry, but it seemed that everyone in the village was accusing one of his sons of killing the swans.

"Moreover, Vicar, it has been told to me that you yourself, as vicar, had personally levelled such an accusation at the head of the lad."

"Nothing of the sort," I said. "There was a large catapult on the river bank. It had an 'R' carved into it. The police have it now. I may have my own idea as to ownership, but anyone who says more is jumping to conclusions."

"Your riverence," he replied grimly, "if one of my lads had done a thing like that, I would have half-murdered him. I cannot say fairer than that, can I?"

"I wish you'd let them all come to Sunday School," I said, changing the subject. "I've called on numerous occasions—but of course, they've had such a lot of illness."

"Illness, your riverence? What illness?"

"The old lady—your mother——"

"The wife's mother, riverence, and a greater trial there has never been for living man to bear."

"She told me the children were ill. They've had measles, whooping cough, scarlet fever, followed by complications, not to mention mumps and chicken-pox. I don't know what they haven't had."

Words trembled on his lips, but he seemed to remember where he was and whom he was addressing. He gulped. "They will all be in perfect health next Sunday, riverence, and they will all be in Sunday School. I give you my word on that, and when I give my word there's no going back. The deed, riverence, is as good as done." He put out a reddish, dirty hand and grasped mine, shaking it without mercy.

I hadn't stopped to 'phone the rural dean for an appointment and if he was surprised to see me again so soon he didn't show it. Once more we faced each other in his study, he still in his wheel-chair.

"I'm awfully sorry to bother you like this, sir," I began, "but I've received this since last we met." I handed him the letter. "I felt I had to come over at once."

He said nothing, reaching for his spectacles and perusing the letter carefully. I watched him anxiously. If only he could help me! But what could he do? Was there any practical way of solving the dilemma? His chat with the wardens must have been too late to make any difference. But would they have taken any notice of it anyway?

At last he laid the paper on his knee and removed his glasses. "Tell me, Insight—what sort of men are your wardens? I've met them, of course, at various church functions but I don't know them."

I spread my hands helplessly. "They've been my friends. At least, I thought they were. What can I tell you about them? Charrington-Hawes is retired. He's extremely wealthy—lives in a great mansion—has rather fixed ideas. But his attitude to the church is absolutely sincere. Jones is a farmer—prosperous—very affable. He'd do anything for anybody. That's what makes it so astounding. I just can't understand it, sir. It doesn't seem to make sense . . . I don't know what to do."

There was silence for a moment and he appeared to be turning things over in his mind. Then he said, "May I make a suggestion, Insight? Two suggestions, really. The first is, do *nothing* to begin with."

"Nothing, sir?"

"Nothing." He acknowledged my surprise. "Let the matter lie. You see, everyone is expecting you to do something—get agitated, draw up letters, become active. But do nothing. Take time to think, to pray and to resolve. As long as you do nothing the reins are in your hand; and that, of course, is where they should be since you are vicar of the parish. If you jump in quickly, however, without first considering your actions then you surrender the advantage to the enem——shall we say to your opponents?"

"Yes, I see, sir." Fool though I might be, I recognised the

wisdom of what he was saying. "But I'll have to reply eventually, won't I?"

He nodded. "But not just yet. Wait. I've done it myself time and again. Never known it to fail."

"It sounds like the right course, sir—but how will I know when to stop doing nothing, to stop waiting?"

"Ah!" he said. "That brings me to my second suggestion. When faced with similar problems myself, while doing nothing with regard to opponents I am at the same time active in other directions. I usually go and have a long chat about it all with someone whom I can trust—someone in the parish. That is always a great help."

"I've been longing to talk to someone, sir—but it seemed that doing so would be disloyal to my wardens."

"Well, Insight, I don't think you need worry about that. There can be no disloyalty in discussing this problem in confidence with a confidant of your own choosing."

"I'd like to feel I could. It's quite impossible for me to approach the wardens. I tried when I apologised and this is the result." I indicated the letter.

"Yes, yes, it would be perfectly all right. Do you know anyone in your parish to whom you could turn?"

"More than one."

"Then that is what I would do. It's such a help."

I couldn't suppress a deep sigh. "It makes it all seem so political, sir. Should a parson be a politician? All he longs to do is to grow in the Christian life, to care for his people, baptise and marry them, visit them when they are ill, help them with their problems—above all to be happy with them. The whole position seems to have changed."

"It *is* political, Insight," he affirmed, reminding me of Mrs. Pankhurst's warning. "You can't avoid it. Wherever there are people there is the body politic, the word 'political' means pertaining to policy. This thing has happened and you need a policy of your own in order to deal with it. Once you've formed that policy you'll be far happier and better equipped to carry on. Where there is no policy there can be no constructive action.

And that is what you and your critics must strive for—constructive action that will heal the breach between you."

"I think I ought to tell the bishop what has happened, sir."

"Certainly."

"And I feel that it's impossible for me to work with my wardens after this. I'd never know whether they were wholly for me after this. I've wounded them badly."

He nodded dubiously. "Yes—but you know the position regarding wardens. In one sense they can't be disposed of; like the Parochial Church Council, they have a continuing life of their own. There is some time to go until the next annual meeting, so you will need much patience and grace . . . Let me know how things progress."

I stood up. "You've helped me tremendously, sir. I feel much better already. It's a ghastly business as far as I'm concerned—but without your advice I'd be completely lost."

"It's kind of you to say so. May we have a prayer together for God's overruling in the whole matter?"

I knelt beside his wheel-chair as he prayed simply to God, trying to concentrate all my thoughts behind his words. I realised, however, that when I rose from my knees it would be to embark on something never before experienced in my ministry—not even in days of upsets and tiffs with Mrs. Fowler and the P.C.C. in London. It was to be nothing less than a political battle; a battle which, as far as I was concerned, could only be fought from the Christian standpoint. And in the field of politics Christianity has not been noticeably successful . . .

During most of my time at St. Hilda's I had visited under difficulties. First there had been the feeling that people disliked me because of the report of my "pagan" speech, and now there was this other trouble. But the visiting had to go on just the same, and I was never sure how much the people knew or what they were thinking. Sometimes I was given a welcome that seemed entirely genuine, while at others it was difficult to disassociate natural village reserve from silent suspicion. It was a great strain.

Shortly after my second visit to the rural dean, I came one afternoon to the house of Mrs. Pankhurst. As usual, she anticipated me.

"I knew you would come," she said, taking me into the now familiar kitchen. "You want to talk."

"It's quite amazing," I replied. "But your prophecy has come true. I've *got* to talk." We settled ourselves at the table. "I have Margaret, of course—but you know why we came here in the first place. She's been getting on so wonderfully. I don't want to start worrying her with parochial problems. She has an idea of what's going on, but she doesn't know how serious it's become. Do you think it's wicked of me to spare her at your expense?"

"Good heavens, no! I'd be furious if you didn't." She rose and started bustling about. "But don't start until you've got some food inside you."

She gave me poached eggs and spinach with fresh bread and butter, followed by tinned peaches and scalding tea. Only when the last morsel had been consumed would she let me begin.

I started to tell her the whole story in sequence. There was no variation. It had become imprinted on my mind like a photograph. I couldn't have changed it if I'd wanted to. But half way through I suddenly stopped.

"You know most of this already, don't you?"

"Yes," she said, "but do go on."

"Why has it happened?" I countered. "There must be something more to it than this. It's building up now almost as if the swans were merely the spark to set the whole thing aflame. What's it all about? Is there something behind it, Mrs. Pankhurst?"

She put down her cup and looked at me steadily. "I think there is."

"Oh, my goodness! What is it?"

"Oh, nothing sinister. It's just that people who live in the country are less—broad-minded, shall we say—than those in the towns. You've got a 'town' mentality, Vicar, and there's bound to be some conflict of views. You take the Rural Dean's advice and talk the whole thing over with someone whose opinion you

5+

respect. Forget what I've said; I'm just a woman and this is a man's problem such as only the massive male mind can solve."

She smiled as she said this but did not ask who my confidant would be. Though she had not said so, I knew I could count on her support if ever I should need it, and I drew comfort from the knowledge.

It was quite late when I left her and made my way back to the vicarage, but already I felt the relief of having talked the matter over.

Nevertheless, I didn't go immediately to see Major Icely the next day. There was another call I'd promised to make, long overdue.

The studio was in the upper part of an old windmill, access to it being by means of ladder-like steps. From the top of these one had a superb treetop-view of the countryside. I stopped to look at it for a moment before turning to knock at the door. But the door was already open and Irene stood there smiling.

"I saw you through the window," she said as I gaped at her in wonder. "Oh!" She looked down at herself. "Do you think I ought to change?"

She was wearing what looked like long black tights that covered every part of her body, hugging her closely from neck to ankles, relieved only by a thin belt of gold at the waist which was clasped by a small gold padlock. Her red hair was swept back behind her ears.

"No—not at all. You—you look very—er—nice," I managed. "I've never actually seen one of those outfits *on* anyone before—except in the newspapers."

She showed me round the studio, telling me that it had become the envy of artists for miles around. "The windmill was going to be demolished, you know; but I saw its possibilities and persuaded Daddy to do something about it. He was able to get it for a song. Aren't I lucky? And I particularly wanted to be in St. Hilda's."

"I can understand why. The scenery here is really beautiful."

She laughed. "But that isn't the reason. Although it *is* lovely here." I must have looked puzzled, for she laughed again. "Can't you guess?"

I shook my head. "Afraid I can't."

"You'll think I'm mad but there's . . . I don't think I'd better tell you."

"You can't stop now. Please. I shall never stop wondering if you don't."

"All right. You'll think it's awfully forward of me but there's someone I'm fond of—is that the word? He doesn't even know I exist. Oh you'll never understand."

"Why not?"

"It's so much easier for a man. I feel guilty just having tried in a roundabout way to make the running. But if I can just see him in the distance from time to time it helps . . ." She was suddenly defenceless in her confidence, appealing. She knelt by the table to pour out tea, her hair so vivid that it drew the eyes like a magnet.

"You could pass a film test, easily, just like that," I said.

"I couldn't. I'm—I'm just ugly."

"Keep thinking that. And you'll stay beautiful."

"You certainly can pay a compliment."

"Well—it's very unlike me really. If I don't honestly feel a thing I couldn't say it. At least I don't think I could."

"You're really surpassing yourself. Have some chocolate biscuits."

"Everyone offers me these things. I love them." So we had our tea, she jumping up every few minutes to shyly slip another canvas on the easel, ask me what I thought of them.

"You don't mind me showing off?" she said.

"I love it. They're awfully good. You have a great gift."

Who could the man be with whom she was in love? Lucky fellow. It couldn't be Bill Tomlinson. Someone like her should have the best.

"And now the one of the church."

"Marvellous. Really marvellous."

"You mustn't have it yet. There are some cloud effects missing —there—see?"

"No. I wouldn't have noticed."

"It's got to be right. I'm sorry but you'll have to wait. I must get it right." She picked up a brush with a very long handle and began to do something with it humming that thing about "Too good to hurry". She swung round. "Now we can talk about *it*."

"About what?" I asked.

"About what I said I wanted to talk to you about—that day by the church. Don't you remember?"

"Yes—that is, no. I do now, but I'd forgotten what it was. What was it?"

"About you being an *author*." The way she pronounced the word alerted something in my mind, but it was nebulous and I let it go.

"Oh."

"You see, when I first said I wanted to talk to you about it I was thrilled at having found out that we had a real, live author in our midst. But I suppose everyone knows now, because it was mentioned in one or two of those recent newspaper reports."

"Yes," I said, something stirring in the back of my mind again, "I hadn't really thought about that. How did you know before this?"

"Well, it was rather funny actually. I was in London for one of those Old Girls' Reunion things—'old girls'!—makes us sound like a lot of octogenarians or something. I was talking about home and all that and mentioned the new vicar. One of the girls said she'd known you in your curate days, or something like that . . ."

"I wonder who it was? What did she look like?"

"She said you'd written two. Have you?"

"Yes."

"I've read them."

"Have you? Did she wear spectacles?"

"Yes—no. No, I don't think she did. Look. You don't want to talk about your writing, do you?"

"I don't mind at all. I wasn't trying to put you off. I was just wondering who it was I knew. I like talking about writing. Anyway, with people who are sympathetic."

"I enjoyed your books."

"As I enjoy your pictures."

"Twin Souls," she said, her eyes twinkling.

"I put words on paper much as you put paint on canvas. Then I study the words and rearrange them and try to present a clear word-picture. If you can write so that people can *see* what you're trying to say, see it as clearly as I can see that picture of yours, it's worth all the struggle and all the work."

The time passed. We made another pot of tea. She suggested we made some toast and sprinkled cheese over it. There were a few apples. I thought of Margaret wrestling with the children and knew I mustn't stop too long. But she sat there hugging her knees.

"Don't go yet," she pleaded, "go on talking. I'll pretend you're you-know-who!"

"I suppose that's a compliment. And I don't know who!"

"Does it ever give you the shivers, after your work is in print, to see something you wish you hadn't written—when it's too late to do anything about it?"

"Sometimes. One time in particular when I wasn't true to myself. In one of the books I gave the impression that I wished one of the characters to call me 'Vicar'. I always regret that. It was a form of pride, I suppose, trying to assert itself —and pride is the most deadly of all the sins. Do you see what I mean?"

"Yes, I think so."

"In actual fact I've never cared two hoots what people call me."

"Haven't you? That's good, because——" She broke off. "I don't know if I ought to tell you. Yes, I will. Why shouldn't I?"

"Tell me what?"

"Well, it was the other day, after you'd been to see Daddy. I'd picked up the telephone in the bedroom to make a call—it's an extension—but Daddy was talking to someone over the main one in the study. I didn't intend to listen, but the man at the other end was talking about you. He was saying it was not right that you should write as you do and that he felt it ought to be taken up with the bishop. I couldn't go on listening, of course—but what did he mean? There was nothing wrong with either of your books."

"I think I can guess who it was," I said, "and what he meant. He was talking about my letter in the papers."

"But he wasn't. He definitely mentioned books, saying that if parsons must write they should confine their energies to theological works." She turned to refill the teapot, and I was glad of a respite. Another piece in my personal jig-saw had just dropped into place, though it was difficult to believe that Charrington-Hawes and the other signatories of the letter objected to my small achievements as an author. Surely not. None of them had ever mentioned it. In fact, it had never occurred to me that they might know about it. After all, why should they? The books, though they sold gratifyingly well, much better than I had ever imagined they would, didn't sweep the country like *Gone With the Wind*. It had seemed most unlikely to me that they could ever have come to the notice of any of the members of my Standing Committee. But even if they had, what possible objection could there be to them. In writing them I had merely tried to write about the church in a simple, human way. There was no crime in that; no breaking of faith with my calling as a parson. Yet from the fragment of conversation Irene had overheard, it seemed that somebody else thought otherwise.

I suddenly knew this was something I had got to think about quietly and seriously. 'Look," I said, getting to my feet, "I'm afraid I'll have to run along now."

"Oh?" She was surprised. "You're not upset because of what I just told you, are you? I didn't mean——"

"No," I said, "it's all right. Actually you've solved a problem that's been puzzling me for quite a while."

She followed me down the steps and walked some way down the lane with me, her black tights contrasting oddly with the country scene. Saying good-bye, I apologised for my abrupt departure, promising to come again soon.

"I hope you will," she said. "It's been lovely. I seem to get on so much better with older men than those of my own age . . ."

On Icely's front door was a small square which lit up when the bell was rung, showing the words "Speak In Here" above a mouthpiece. It was all part of another of his labour-saving gadgets, this time to save him from continually rushing to the door when people called. When the caller had announced himself, Icely would press a button which released the front door.

"It's me—Insight," I said into the aperture self-consciously. It always made me feel slightly ridiculous. "May I see you?"

"Come in, old boy," came Icely's voice from the living-room. "Glad to see you. Was going to 'phone you, as a matter of fact."

He settled me comfortably, seeming to sense suddenly that this was rather more than just a casual visit, bringing me an extra cushion for the chair and a stool to put my feet on. Then he sat back himself, leaving me to make my own opening.

Once again I told my story, first explaining that the rural dean had suggested I consult someone I could trust. He made no comment, but his face became grim. When I came to the part about my reacting in anger to Charrington-Hawes' announcement that he was calling a meeting, however, he couldn't refrain from voicing his opinion.

"I should jolly well think so, Padre. You must have been utterly infuriated."

"I was. Almost uncontrollably, I'm afraid, and I felt deeply ashamed afterwards. But at the time it seemed to me that to call a meeting with the purpose of censuring me in my absence was quite scandalous. Perhaps if I had been less incensed things would have turned out differently, though I did apologise for my ill-manners at the first opportunity." I pulled the document from my pocket and handed it to him. "That's all—except that I must make a reply some time."

When he'd read the paper he said, "I was approached about

this meeting. Charrington-Hawes rang me to say that a few of them were getting together to discuss the article in the press. They wanted me to be with them."

"What then?"

"You know me. I like to know what I'm getting into. 'The vicar will be there, of course, won't he?' I said. 'If the meeting concerns him . . .' 'No,' says Charrington-Hawes. 'He hasn't been asked.' Well, you can imagine . . . I told him that life was pretty hectic at the moment and I wouldn't have the time. He didn't press me. I don't think he expected he'd have much success with me."

"If he'd got you," I said, "he'd have had the whole Standing Committee. Look at the names at the bottom of the sheet."

Together we explored every angle of the problem. Should I call on Charrington-Hawes or should I write to him? Ought I to summon a meeting? Always we came back to the fact that the rural dean's advice was sound—to do nothing until a way opened. There was no hurry. I was the vicar and it was up to me to choose the moment for action. The only danger was that if I left it too long the initiative might swing to the other side. The discussion was valuable and Icely was discreet. Charrington-Hawes and Jones were still the wardens and, however deeply he might have felt the irregularity of the meeting, he expressed little by way of criticism.

"I'll be seeing the bishop any day now," I told him. "I've sent him copies of the letter and the statement and asked for an appointment. I'm coming round to the feeling, though, that any statement I may make ought to be through the normal constitutional channels; that would mean at the next Standing Committee."

"After that," he said, smiling, "it would follow on to the Parochial Church Council and possibly the annual meeting. But for the moment, Jim, shall we go on thinking and, if anything fresh occurs to either of us, have another talk? Any time you wish me to summon the Standing Committee I'll do it. As secretary to the P.C.C. that's part of my job."

As I walked back to the vicarage, the peace of the countryside was all about—an incongruous setting for this great quarrel. The talk, however, had been a tonic; and Icely was my friend.

Just after supper he was on the 'phone to tell me that Charrington-Hawes had rung him shortly after I'd left. There had been some church matter Charrington-Hawes had wished to discuss and then, as if it were of no great consequence, he had mentioned the meeting.

"I didn't say that I'd just seen you and knew all about it," Icely chuckled. "He said that what none of them could make out was why the vicar hadn't replied to a message they'd sent him and which he must surely have received by now. I said airily that he shouldn't worry and that you'd probably make some reply at the next meeting. 'Meeting?' he said. 'What meeting?' 'The Standing Committee,' I said. There was a long silence and I wondered if he'd fainted or something." He chuckled again. "When he did speak, he said that a public reply from you would be quite out of the question. The meeting and the message had been confidential and the vicar would certainly have no wish to reply in public."

"Oh, wouldn't I?" I said.

"Exactly. You're one up already. If it's possible to tell how a man reacts at the far end of a telephone wire, I'd say—in boxing parlance—that I'd landed a beauty right over the heart. He sounded completely taken aback."

Replacing the receiver, I sat back with a feeling of satisfaction —the satisfaction any politician must feel after a successful manœuvre. And I chuckled. Whether the satisfaction or the chuckle were exactly Christian was something my conscience would have to tussle with at a later date.

★ 10 ★

PICKING up my papers from his desk, the bishop pursed his lips. He seemed to be hypnotised by his inkstand but managed to tear his eyes from it at last and look at me.

"Got yourself into a bit of a mess, haven't you?" he said. "What do you intend doing about it?"

"I thought that perhaps you could advise me, my lord."

"Mmm ... These people here whose names are on the sheet—who are they?"

"All the Standing Committee, except for one who refused to attend the meeting."

"You don't want to have them all against you, do you?"

"Indeed not, my lord. While this goes on we can't get down to much spiritual work. I was wondering if I could get some new wardens."

He gave me a long look. "Why? You may not care for the way they handled this matter, but they were perfectly within their rights. They're not thinking of resigning, I suppose?"

"No, sir. It would make all the difference if they did."

We sat in silence and the thought crossed my mind that he didn't really know how to advise me. I decided to make one last effort.

"Don't you think, my lord, that all this business is political and the only way to handle it, even though we are a Christian congregation, is in a political manner?"

He raised a purple-clad arm and scratched at his ear. "Political, Insight? I don't quite follow. Surely this is nothing to do with politics." It was almost possible to see him thinking the names of the parties—Tories, Socialists, Liberals—puzzling it all out, wondering where they came into it. The only thing for me was to try and handle the situation myself and, for the moment, salvage what I could from the wreck of the appointment.

"You don't think I've done wrong, my lord?"

"No. It's just a clash of opinions, but they're as much entitled to their view as you are to yours. We don't want to anger them needlessly. Perhaps you should carry on till Easter and then intimate tactfully to your own warden that you would like a change, and try another man."

"Yes, my lord."

Not wishing to press the point any further, I told him about Mrs. Markesete and her desire for confirmation. He said that he would be delighted to come and gladly take the service in her bedroom, fixing the date and time there and then.

Depressed, I returned to St. Hilda's determined to do something concrete without any more consultations. First I would ascertain exactly what the law was regarding wardens, and then I would draft a reply to be given at the next Standing Committee. There was no other way in which to reply. I was not going to treat with an unconstitutional body such as had been called together by Charrington-Hawes. When I'd done both these things I'd talk again with Icely.

There was a book on church law* in my study and, finding the chapter headed "The Churchwardens and Sidesmen", I read as follows:

"The usual number of churchwardens is two, and Canon 89 implies that there shall be two. A custom that there shall be more than two churchwardens, or even one only, will be good; but a custom that there shall be no churchwardens is bad.

"Any person who is qualified to be a member of the parochial church council may be a churchwarden but this is without prejudice to 'existing qualifications', and therefore in ancient parishes any householder (or perhaps resident) is eligible. A woman may be a churchwarden. In parishes in which before 1921 one or more churchwardens were elected by the vestry, they are now elected by a joint meeting of the vestry and the persons whose names are on the electoral roll, and the consent of the incumbent must be given to their choice; but if the incumbent and meeting cannot agree on the choice of churchwardens, one is elected by

* *The Law of the Parish Church*, W. L. Dale.

the meeting and the other nominated by the incumbent. There may be in a particular parish a special custom as to the election of churchwardens, which will hold good if clearly proved ...

"After election or nomination the churchwardens are admitted to office by the bishop or archdeacon on his visitation, when they make a declaration that they will faithfully and diligently perform the duties of their office, and until they are so admitted their predecessors remain in office and they themselves are not legally churchwardens."

I read on, flicking the pages, learning that the duties of wardens related to the collection of alms, disposal of the communion alms, the maintenance of order, the allocation of seats, the parochial registers, the protection of the church property, by action if necessary, and the guardianship of the interests of the church against all forms of wrongdoing. If there was any neglect of duty or impropriety on the part of the incumbent or the officers of the church then it was the duty of the wardens to inform the bishop.

I discovered that if for any reason the parishioners get so annoyed with their vicar that they feel something must be done and they wish to have a meeting, they may only take action if a third of the members of the P.C.C. put their signatures to such a request and present it to the archdeacon. If the archdeacon deems there is sufficient cause for such a gathering, he may then convene an extraordinary meeting of the council and either take the chair himself or appoint someone to represent him.

Refreshed with these facts and points of procedure, it seemed to me that the intention of the Canon of 1603 concerning the election of churchwardens was that there should be, above all else, unity in a church and congregation.

One thing was quite clear. No one could force either Charrington-Hawes or Jones to resign. Neither seemed to have the slightest intention of taking such a step, and it looked as though I would have to grit my teeth and hang on until the annual meeting. Then, with luck and the agreement of the meeting, I might be able to have two men after my own heart. The form was that the wardens should be elected if possible by the joint consent of the people and their vicar. Failing such agreement, the vicar was free to appoint one man—who became known as the Vicar's Warden—and the people would make their own choice by vote—their man being the People's Warden. If it came to that, there was the strong possibility of either Charrington-Hawes or Jones being elected once again. It was disquieting because, as I well knew, both were excellent men. It was a thousand pities I had got across them, but short of self-betrayal there was nothing I could do.

It was time to set to work on my reply. With the happenings of the past weeks fresh in my mind, boosted by my newly acquired legal knowledge, I reached for pen and paper.

When Margaret came in with a glass of milk and the suggestion that I should leave whatever I was doing until the morning, it was much later than I'd realised. But I was too wound up to let things lie and I went on writing long after she'd gone to bed. Finally, at about two thirty in the morning, I slouched back in my chair to read what I'd written. If it seemed satisfactory, I would let Icely have it for his comment. After the date and the heading "Statement to Standing Committee" it ran as follows:

"I recently received a joint-letter from a number of people expressing concern about certain actions of mine. I would like to make some reply.

On coming not very long ago to St. Hilda's, I determined to carry on the work here in as helpful and spiritual a manner as possible. My wife and I received a warm welcome and believed that the congregation and parish were in favour of what we were determined to do.

Not long ago a swan's nest in the river at the bottom of the Vicarage glebe was destroyed. Immediately after this was done I saw the damage and knew that it was the work of children. The scene so distressed me that I was convinced we ought to make the matter widely known. I therefore wrote a letter to the local paper and this later received wide prominence. As far as I am concerned I still stand by what I wrote then and do not wish to retract anything.

The vicar of a parish does not need to ask for permission if he wishes to write on a matter he considers important. Only by trying to enlist popular indignation against those who did this thing could we prevent it happening again. As you know, young people are constantly doing things which we regret. However, does the position not often deteriorate because of our unwillingness to take any action?

This, then, was the sole reason for my taking action. As to the publicity received, I can only say that it has made no difference to my feelings and there are people who agree with me that what I did was right.

The most distressing part of the whole business is that some members of our congregation feel I have done wrong, and letters I have received implied that I should not have written my letter without first consulting church officials.

It is becoming increasingly obvious that I no longer have the full confidence of those elected to help run church affairs. Where this occurs in a church there is laid down a constitutional method for expressing displeasure if it gets beyond the bounds of toleration. One third of the P.C.C. must approach the archdeacon with a view to holding a meeting. If the archdeacon finds there is substance in the request, he may grant such a request. If this correct method had been taken I would have made no objection. Indeed I firmly believe the archdeacon would not have seen fit to grant the necessary permission.

With regard to the letters sent me, the chief cause of contention seems to have been that I attacked all the children of St. Hilda's church and village. Indeed from conversations with some of you I gather the popular belief is that I branded them all as hooligans. This is just not true. I wrote about one specific incident in the hope that parents would in future be more careful to oversee the activities of their children.

Someone even suggested that my wife and I do not look after our own children and that my son Robert was lost for a time. It is true that he was lost, but to link this running away of a small boy of five with a deliberate attack by older children on a swan's nest seems to me to be absurd."

I paused to read what I had written. It sounded stiff and even self-righteous, but I had to make some reply. I needed in some way to convey to my opponents (how awful to call them that) that if meetings were to be called then it must be in a constitutional fashion. I set to work to finish the statement in as friendly a manner as possible.

"May I suggest then, that in future we work through the normal channels, and that I am allowed to express myself, as indeed all of you are, through the medium of the spoken and written word. We want surely to forget our differences and enjoy ourselves together in the service of God. My only regret is that this unfortunate difference of opinion should have arisen."

The Standing Committee need only consist of the vicar and the two churchwardens. In many churches, and this was the case in St. Hilda's, additional members are elected by the P.C.C. Its purpose is to deal with any parochial matter that calls for speedy consideration. In our own case, it was usual for us to meet a week before the P.C.C. meeting and discuss a number of subjects that would be coming up before the council.

Used correctly, the Standing Committee can be a valuable asset. It may not, however, be called together by anyone except the vicar. It was all very well for Charrington-Hawes to state that the meeting he had called in response to various requests was not a meeting of the Standing Committee as such—that it was a meeting of private individuals and had no authority or purpose other than to put their collective views before the vicar. He had, in fact, called together the Standing Committee without my permission, taking my place himself as chairman. It was almost childishly ridiculous but, because he was a warden and would remain a warden at least until the Annual General Meeting, something had to be done to counteract his move. What other vicars would have done in similar circumstances I couldn't know. But I did know that the worry involved was eating into my heart and soul and, worst of all, I couldn't hide it from Margaret. I should have known that I couldn't prevent her from involving herself in my troubles, and already some of the recent sparkle was leaving her. Country air wouldn't make up for peace of mind and I dreaded the thought of her health suffering again because of all this. My mind seemed to be in a constant whirl.

Icely approved of my reply and advocated immediate action. I was glad of this. The longer I waited the more I would torture myself with doubts, conjectures and forebodings. Better to get the whole thing done with as soon as possible. So it was agreed that a meeting of the Standing Committee should be convened two days hence.

When the time came I was early at the church, only to find that Quimbolt had done nothing about preparing the place despite the fact that he'd been specifically asked to do so. He had been growing increasingly difficult recently, showing only too clearly whose side he was on. Since he was salaried, however, there was a limit to how far he could go. He knew that he could very easily be sent packing if he overstepped the mark. There would be a reasonable excuse for his deficiency, as usual.

The Committee was to meet in the church vestry, and I set the chairs in place around the table as the members started to arrive. They each greeted me, but I sensed a stiffness and lack of affability that chilled me. It seemed impossible that I could ever again be happy and relaxed with them, knowing that they had met and discussed me behind my back. All that could be said in mitigation was that none of them could have any idea of how much their action had hurt me.

It wanted a minute or two to the hour and we sat around waiting for the last arrivals, no one saying very much. My reply was in my pocket and only Icely, who had not yet arrived, knew what I intended to do. I had the sinking feeling that one gets before a vital examination.

Icely arrived on the dot, looking extremely cheerful. He took the minute book from beneath his arm and placed it on the table. Then he whirled round the table offering everyone a toffee from a bag he'd produced from his pocket. When he'd returned to his place, we stood while I opened with a prayer. Hardly anyone seemed to say "Amen" and this annoyed me, until I realised that most of them had accepted one of Icely's toffees and probably couldn't get their jaws open.

Briskly, Icely read the minutes of the last meeting, and there was some preliminary discussion of one or two small matters. Then the moment was upon me. I had to go over the top. None of them could know the agony inside me. All I wanted was to pray and worship and love and serve our Lord with each and every one of them. But instead, they'd forced me into this political battle, a thing repugnant to both my nature and my calling. That they had a case, I just could not believe. There was no other course open to me than to meet them as firmly and as spiritually as possible.

Producing my reply, I placed it on the table before me. Then I heard my own voice as if from a great distance. "Before we deal with the agenda there is something I would like to say." All eyes were on me and I read the statement slowly and carefully. When it was done there was silence. Then Charrington-Hawes crossed his legs and folded his arms.

"Well, Vicar," he said, "I said I was no yes-man. If you want wardens then you must expect them to voice their own feelings and the feelings of those whom they represent..." His voice rattled on, but such was the turmoil in my mind at the effort it had cost me to produce my reply that I couldn't take in exactly what he was saying. I tried, however, to give the impression that I understood the points he was making. "But what about the others?" I heard him say. "What do you all feel?"

There were mumbled comments but no one seemed to want to make a speech about it. The only impression it gave me was that they were all still against me. My carefully prepared statement had been as effective as leaves against the wind. It was hard to know what I had expected would happen as a result of my words—apologies, perhaps—a vote of confidence—regrets—a truce, at least. But there was no indication that the situation altered one whit. No one showed any regret for his part in the secret meeting. Saigon said something about the unfortunate impression my letter had created, and I replied that the truth was what mattered. And that was about all.

Since there was no prolonged discussion and no one seemed eager to commit himself, I said, "If no one wishes to say anything further, perhaps we had better continue with the agenda."

"Just a minute," said Icely, speaking for the first time. "There's something I'd like to know." He turned to Charrington-Hawes. "What on earth made it necessary for you to hold that meeting at all?"

"I should have thought," Charrington-Hawes replied coldly, "that that was already abundantly clear. Both Mr. Jones and I were being continually asked what we were going to do. It was our duty to do something. We did it."

Icely was on the point of making a heated reply but seemed to think better of it. He relapsed into silence and we went on to deal with the rest of the agenda.

For the remainder of that meeting I scarcely knew what was happening. Lost in thought, I replied automatically when it was expected of me. My mind was occupied with going over and over the steps I had taken. Meanwhile two of the members became quite pugnacious and arbitrary, telling each other that they would do this or that in some matter that was of little consequence. Doodling on my agenda paper, I had lost control of the meeting. This was defeat. The Committee was triumphant.

When the discussion was over I said meekly, "Shall we close by saying the Grace together?" and when that was done the meeting broke up. I stood apart. No one came and spoke to me and, at that moment, I had no wish to talk to any of them. We were now in the realm of politics rather than Christianity. I had rejoiced in the blow over the heart received by Charrington-Hawes. Now it was my turn to receive a smashing upper-cut from the floor. It had ripped into me, leaving me helpless, gasping, defenceless. I was no politician, that much was clear. I'd had all the aces—yet what had I done? I could have lashed them with charges of unspirituality, their alliance with Dathan and Abiram and their sure preparation for the fires of God, all of which in that moment of unbalanced reasoning I felt to be true. Yet here they were, triumphant, talking confidently to one another, pleased and proud, probably going away to hatch further plots. Oh, Heavens, I was becoming hysterical!

When the rest of them had gone, Icely crossed to my side. His customary cheerfulness seemed to have deserted him.

"Not so good, was it?" he said.

I shook my head, too full to answer him.

"Never mind," he continued. "It could be that C.H. is playing his hand more cleverly than we realise. You can't deny his integrity. Whatever we may think of his recent action, there is no doubt in his own mind that his handling of the situation is beyond reproach. And most of the others gladly follow his lead. My guess is that he was shaken by your bringing this matter into the open by making your reply publicly to the Standing Committee. He's not a man to compromise with his conscience. Clearly he believed some action to be necessary and by handling it the way he did, he hoped to make his protest and let it rest there. It's my belief that he said very little to-night on the principle of least said soonest mended."

"That's fine," I said bitterly. "He's satisfied his own conscience, but what about mine? Or aren't I allowed to have one?"

"Things would be a lot easier if you hadn't, Jim. You know, for a mild-mannered man there's a surprising lot of sand in your make-up. Stick to your guns, my lad. You may not win this campaign, but at least you'll come out of it with honour."

Scarcely twenty-four hours had passed, but Mrs. Pankhurst knew exactly what had happened at the meeting. And she was angry.

"The trouble is," she said, "you're not firm enough."

"My reply didn't mince matters."

"It hasn't convinced them. Given time it will get home, but I'm afraid you'll weaken before then."

"I shouldn't be surprised. I can't fight people. As I've told you before, I'm not a politician. I'm shy and I'm nervous."

She became quite fierce, making me sit down and listen to her.

"You've got to fight, Vicar. Not because I think you are right or wrong, but because you've got to keep faith with yourself. Believing yourself to be right, you will never rest again if you backed down now." She became, as she often chose to be, deliberately shocking. "Do you think I'd be seen dead with that lot on the Standing Committee? A complete bunch of dead-beats if ever I saw one. And I'll tell you something else——" She was so vehement that I began to smile. "Don't laugh—it's true; some of those washed-in-the-blood Christians are the least tolerant of all of God's creatures. Ever seen their mouths set into thin hard lines?"

I laughed aloud. "You're quite absurd," I said.

"Am I? Well, all I can say is that I'm thankful I'm an Anglo-Catholic. Judas was an Evangelical."

"And so am I."

"But you're different. There's nothing bigoted in your conception of the Lord's work. You don't criticise me because I cross myself and genuflect in St. Hilda's, do you?"

"Of course not."

"Why not?"

"Because I mentally cross myself quite a bit. It makes sense. I want to be covered by the doctrine of the Cross."

"You'll be an Anglo one day, Vicar. I'm sure you will."

"I doubt it—unless they change some of their doctrines."

"There's one thing they *do* have, and that's a respect for the priesthood. You'd never get this kind of thing happening in an Anglo-Catholic church. We're too low at St. Hilda's."

"Priests *can* be wrong," I said.

"Good grief!" she exclaimed. "Whose side are you on? Do you know what Danny calls you?"

"Yes."

"The anointed of the Lord," she quoted.

"I know. It embarrasses me."

"Well, it mustn't. It mustn't." Her integrity was beyond question, her masculinity giving her words a depth that might have been missing in one more feminine.

"I wish you'd come on some of these working committees," I said. "Let yourself be put up at the Annual Meeting for the new P.C.C. I know it's still some distance away, but it would encourage me. I'd know I had you as a friend anyway."

"You have plenty of friends on the P.C.C."

"You've just been telling me I've got to fight, but you won't come in and fight with me."

I could see that I had scored.

"I'll think about it," she said. "I vowed I never would . . . But don't think I'm not doing what I can behind the scenes. The Standing Committee won't have it all their own way when the P.C.C. meets."

"Why did you vow you never would?" I wanted to know.

"Because I've sat on church committees in the past. I'm not one for bandying words, you know. What I have to say, I say. And all the good it ever seemed to do was antagonise people."

"But you will think about it?"

"Yes," she said with a sudden smile, "I'll think about it."

On Sunday I dropped in at the local schoolroom where Sunday School classes were held. Two sisters named Etranger led the school. They wore clothes which conjured up memories of a past age, with brimmed hats set squarely on their brown hair. Due to recent changes in women's fashions, however, their way of dressing was in danger of becoming absolutely up-to-date. Whenever one met them they appeared to be standing very close together, speaking almost with one voice. My arrival coincided with a small crisis and their relief at my appearance was tremendous.

"Thank goodness you're here, Vicar," said one, or both, of them. "Valerie and Joyce say they've lost some of their belongings—and they won't let Felicity go. What are we to do?"

I hadn't a clue so I tried to look cheerful. "Well, well, well!" I said. "Let's see if we can sort it all out."

"We've lost things, too," said a group of other children, putting up their hands as if they were still in school.

"It's dreadful!" said the Misses Etranger together.

Felicity, the centre of attention, was about nine or ten years of age; a big girl, her body straining at a dirty cotton frock.

"Perhaps you picked something up by mistake," I suggested, turning to her. "It could happen to anyone."

"No, I didn't," she said, shaking her head. There was unmistakable candour in her blue eyes. In view of the accusations of the other children, it was understandable that her cheeks should be very red.

"I'm sure I've seen you somewhere before, Felicity," I said kindly. "What's your other name?"

"Rafferty."

"They all came," one of the Etrangers put in. "We weren't expecting them at all. They just arrived!"

One of the accusers said, "She's taken our things. We know she has." Some of the others seemed to be guarding the door. I couldn't see any other Raffertys and could only presume they'd made off as soon as the class finished. It was hard to know what to do. Felicity seemed determined to maintain her innocence and I certainly couldn't accuse her without proof positive.

"Are you quite sure?" I asked her again.

"Yes," she replied. "Quite sure."

"Well, then." I made a move. "Let's have a look round the room."

The children didn't stir, standing with their eyes fixed on Felicity. One of them put out a hand as if to restrain the girl, but she shook it off. Then, suddenly and unexpectedly, Felicity walked straight through the circle around her and opened a desk. Inside were a number of small objects of the comb, purse and bracelet variety. These were swooped upon by the youngsters, and when we looked back for Felicity she was no longer in the room. One Miss Etranger shooed the youngsters out, while the other turned to me.

"We knew she'd done it," she said, "but we couldn't prove it. We were so surprised to see all those Raffertys. We can't think why they came. They've never been before—even though Mr. Bigwood tried so hard. We do hope they never come again."

"What? They're just the children we want."

The other Miss Etranger had come back and now I wasn't

sure which of them was actually doing the talking. Whichever
it was said, "Not if they behave like that."

"Like what?"

"Taking things and so on. During the talk they were whisper-
ing together and giggling. It *has* upset us."

"They're sort of black sheep, are they?"

"Oh, yes, Vicar. Very, very black."

"But didn't Christ say those were the people He wanted? He
didn't come, He said, for the righteous."

They saw the point but just stood there, wrinkling their brows
and looking worried. With those hats, I thought, they looked
like mushrooms. Eventually one of them said, "If we have them,
we'll lose all the others." She spoke gently, without bitterness.
"The children will tell their parents all about this. If the
Raffertys continue to come, the parents of the other children
will refuse to allow them to come. We shan't have any Sunday
School at all."

That, I thought, might not be such a dreadful thing. Perhaps
a few parents might then decide to bring their children to church
for a change. But I couldn't say this. It certainly wouldn't be
understood. Instead I said, "It's difficult, I know; but I'm sure
you'll agree that we can't turn children away."

"No . . ." they chorused doubtfully.

"We don't think they really enjoyed being here," said one
of them.

"That's true," said the other, brightening. "Perhaps—perhaps
after this afternoon's excitement they'll decide not to come
again . . ."

The bishop had been and departed. The soul of kindness, his
voice had been quiet and soothing in the publican's bedroom in
keeping with the great solemnity that attends a confirmation in
a sick room. Mr. Markesete, whose devotion to his wife showed
in his every action, was deeply moved.

"I hope I didn't do wrong, Vicar," he said as we stood in the
roadway watching the bishop's car out of sight, "but I had a
quiet word with the bishop's chauffeur. I said no offence was

meant but would he allow me to place a case of champagne in the boot of the Bishop's car. Perhaps he could explain the situation to the Bishop on the journey home. If his Grace ..."

"His lordship," I corrected automatically.

"If his lordship didn't like champagne perhaps someone else might..."

"I'm sure it will be appreciated."

"And I'd like to send a cheque as well, sir, for all his lordship's kindness, but I'm so ignorant in these matters. If you could help me..." He went straight on to tackle another subject, equally difficult. "There's something else, too, sir. If ever you need any help in your church meetings, would you please let me know? I hope I'm not talking out of turn, but I can't help hearing all sorts of rumours in my job. A lot of my customers may not be regular churchgoers, but they're baptised; and if it was a matter of voting—well, they know how they'd like to place their votes." He paused. "This isn't my idea, sir. They wanted me to let you know."

"Thank you very much," I said sincerely.

We then talked about his wife and the confirmation. He felt it had made a great difference to her to have had the bishop come here especially for her.

"It will make things easier to face," he murmured. "You know..."

"She's a very sick woman," I said.

"Yes, sir."

"She——" I hesitated. It wasn't going to be easy to say.

"She—she's dying. Is that what you wanted to tell me, sir?"

"I'm afraid so."

"I—know..." His face crumpled and, so as not to break down completely before me, he turned and hurried away.

A clergyman's life might well be likened to an emotional see-saw. Unlike a doctor, his interest in his "patients" should not be impersonal—yet he must be prepared to hurry from ministering to the dying to blessing the new born, from arranging a funeral to planning a wedding. He never knows what may crop up or who might call and for what purpose.

The couple at the door were young—he with the cherry red cheeks and bull neck of the countryman and she fair, still in the plumpness of youth. At a guess, she milked cows. They both stood looking at me, neither saying a word.

"Do come in if you want to see me," I said, leading them to the study.

It could have been banns or baptism and I sat with them, waiting for someone to say something. At last the man spoke.

"Name's Challump."

"Oh, yes . . . ?" I said, showing that I was eager to hear more. It was an unusual name, but most of the names around St. Hilda's were unusual.

Again we waited in silence, rather like at a seance. Just when the table might have been expected to rise, Challump made another statement.

"She's pregnant."

"Ah! Congratulations," I said. We looked at the girl, who put her hands in her lap and took to studying them. "I'll get you a baptismal form. It's a good thing to get it settled well in advance."

Challump shook his head. "We want to get married."

"Oh!"

"We want you to marry us. Will you?"

"Well," I said, reassembling my thoughts, "if I were to conduct the ceremony I'd need some assurance that you were truly penit—— er—sorry for what you had done. You see, it makes us look a bit silly praying that you may be fruitful when we know already that you are expecting a child. You're supposed to get married first and then have the baby. That's the correct order."

"She's sorry," said Challump. "Aren't you?"

The girl nodded, disinclined to take part in the conversation, hardly daring to life her eyes. She seemed quite literally to be a dumb blonde.

I went into the theological definition of being sorry in God's sight without being able to tell whether or not they understood. They agreed to everything, even joining in a prayer and saying the words after me. I said the absolution and then presented them with a marriage application form, taking back the baptismal one, and saying, "You could come and see me later about this."

The interview was concluded but the couple made no move to go. A significant look passed between them and then Challump said, "Can she be married in white?"

"You mean after what's happened? White being the colour of purity?"

He turned to the girl. "You won't change your mind, will you?"

She shook her head.

"I have no control," I said, "over what people wear in church. God looks on your heart, not on your clothes. You must wear whatever you think suitable."

"It's my brother," Challump explained. "If she wears white at her wedding, us'll have awful trouble. He's sworn to get up and say something in church."

"But he mustn't do that!"

"Can't stop him. He's determined."

"Well, I'm glad you told me. We can take precautions—have a word with the police and, if anything happens, remove him quickly. The last thing we want is a scene in church."

He nodded his agreement.

"The first thing you must do, Mr. Challump," I urged, "is go and see your brother. Tell him tactfully what I've said. Get the family to see reason."

They stood up, Challump folding the marriage form and putting it in his pocket. "Very grateful, Vicar," he said. "I'll do what you say—but I know my brother. It won't change him."

I walked with them to the front door.

"Why," I asked, "do you think it will be impossible to make your brother see reason?"

Challump turned on the doorstep and chuckled.

"Because I did it to him at his wedding."

"You did what?"

"Spoke out. His missus was the same way and I said it was wrong to get married in white. He's sworn to get even with me."

"Yes," I said, horrified, "but you didn't actually protest in church!"

"I started to, but before I could finish Mr. Bigwood—he wasn't like you—shot down the aisle and said if he had any more of my nonsense he'd throw me out of the church himself. He *was* annoyed. So I shut up."

As I gaped at them, speechless, they started down the drive. It took me a moment to find my voice, and then I called after their retreating forms, weakly but hopefully, "Blue is a very attractive colour . . ."

★ II ★

"THINGS are never as bad as one imagines they're going to be," said Margaret as I was leaving the vicarage for the P.C.C. meeting. She kissed me. "Do stop worrying, darling, please."

"All right," I replied, with the best I could do in the way of a smile, "as of this moment."

I left her standing in the doorway, conscious that she was watching me and knowing that she was worried too.

The Parochial Church Council is an advisory body, its primary duty being to co-operate with the minister in the initiation, conduct and development of the church work both within the parish and outside. How much co-operation I could now expect was problematic. It was impossible not to worry. There was no way of knowing which way the wind would blow when my controversy with the wardens was raised.

After the Standing Committee meeting fiasco, Icely had conjectured that Charrington-Hawes might not expect me to raise the matter again at this meeting. It was the sort of thing that one is liable to say without thinking. Soon afterwards we both realised, as Charrington-Hawes must have done, that the whole thing would come up automatically since the minutes of the Standing Committee would be read to the Council. It was, in fact, precisely what I'd intended. Now, though, I wasn't at all sure that I had the moral strength to face another defeat.

My relations with the wardens had become so strained that every meeting with them during the normal running of the church was a trial. The atmosphere between us seemed anything but Christian and it gnawed at my conscience. Only one course could have won them back—a retraction of what I had written, an apology for what I had done. But I had searched my heart and found such a course impossible. It would have been untrue to myself and my faith.

As I entered the church hall I heard a man in a group say quite distinctly to one of the others, "Whose side are you on?" It reminded me that, no matter how I might look on it, the whole thing was really political; and I wondered suddenly how David would have handled it. But David would never have let it get to this state.

When the meeting began, I doodled while Icely read slowly and deliberately. Every word of the statement sent to me by the unofficial gathering and my reply to it sank into listening ears. It was no longer private or confidential. At the conclusion of my reply there was a buzz of excited comment and the meeting had to be called to order while Icely finished reading the minutes. It was not until we came to "Matters Arising" that anything could be said. Then Thomas, the principal of the College at which I taught, said that this was the first he'd heard of the matter. He was a discreet man, too retiring to become immersed in village or church controversy.

I took the opportunity of explaining what had happened, going over the ground once more—the old ground I knew so well. When I spoke of reacting angrily to the wardens' declaration that a meeting would be held, a voice cried out loudly, "Of course!" Another said, "Hear, hear!" It was heartening to know that some of them agreed with me.

Before anyone else could say anything, Saigon rose and suggested that the best thing would be to forget the whole thing. "There is surely," he propounded, "more than enough strife in these troublesome times. Are there any lengths to which we should not go in order to achieve and preserve peace?" My heart warmed to him; it was so much what I wanted. It would have been a wonderful note on which to close, but the Council was not going to be done out of its discussion. Some wanted to go back as far as the almost-forgotten swans, others were more concerned about the hooligan children. If it came no nearer to actually solving the problem, at least a new atmosphere could be sensed. The political climate was brightening. I was not without support. There seemed to be a general feeling that, even though acting from the noblest sentiments, Charrington-Hawes really

shouldn't have called a meeting behind my back. It didn't neces-
sarily mean that they thought I was right but merely that they
acknowledged he might have been wrong. Nevertheless, it was
a step forward.

Then Charrington-Hawes stood up. As my warden he was
sitting just to my right. His movement brought about an instant
hush and everyone looked at him.

"When I first met the Vicar," he said, "I made it quite clear
that I was a man who followed his own lead. If I believe a thing
is right, I say so. If I believe it to be wrong, then I say so. Some
of you may think that because I bear the title 'Vicar's Warden'
I have to do exactly what the Vicar wishes. That is not how I
see the office of a warden."

He went on to make a fluent speech in which he explained
what a shock it had been to him to find all this news about the
children placarded all over the place when he himself had not
been consulted. "If," he said firmly, "the Vicar expects me to
give him my support, one would have thought that he could
have asked my advice before penning his letter. What is sauce
for the goose is sauce for the gander. Those of you with indepen-
dent minds will appreciate the dilemma in which I found myself.
I do not consider it disloyal to the Vicar to oppose him on the
present issue. Just as he is convinced that what he has done is
right, so am I satisfied concerning my own actions."

When he sat down you could have heard a pin drop, so per-
suasively had he held the attention of his audience. Then the
silence was broken by the scraping of Jones' heavy boots across
the bare floor as he rose to his feet. As a speaker Jones lacked
Charrington-Hawes' grace and polish, but he made up for it
in a down-to-earth directness that was no less effective in its way.
He spoke of the concern of the village as a whole and of the
parents in particular; of the urgent demand that a public meeting be held so that all could voice their displeasure.

As he said this, Icely leapt to his feet and interrupted. "A
public meeting, Mr. Jones? Who of the public were invited to
attend? If you look at the list of signatories on the document of
which the Vicar complains, ladies and gentlemen, you'll find

only the names of members of the Standing Committee. And they attended by invitation; I know that because I was among those invited. So how can you possibly call it a public meeting? And if this does not convince you, tell me how you can hold a public meeting of which the findings are private and confidential —as those outlined in this famous document purported to be."

He sat down and a buzz of excitement ran through the room. Mr. Jones, who had remained standing, waited for silence, unperturbed. "If the Major had allowed me to finish what I was saying," he went on, at last, "I would have saved him the trouble of asking his questions. I repeat, there was a strong demand for a public meeting, but Mr. Charrington-Hawes, myself and other friends of the Vicar were against this washing of dirty linen in public. We were of the opinion that no good could come of it and, moreover, if the newshounds of Fleet Street had got to hear of it we should again have found ourselves spot-lighted in undesirable publicity.

"We therefore adopted the traditional British expedient of compromise. We called a meeting, but, as Major Icely has told you, admittance was by invitation only. Invitations were restricted to members of the Standing Committee as being those people of this village most concerned about our church and, if I may say so, the fair name of our Vicar. Was this really the heinous crime that Mr. Insight would have us believe?"

Remaining seated, Icely answered him.

"Nobody's mentioned the word 'crime', Mr. Jones, so let's save the dramatics for a more suitable occasion. What the Vicar has said, however, and with every justification, is that your action in calling a meeting of the Standing Committee was thoroughly unconstitutional. Neither you, nor Mr. Charrington-Hawes, nor indeed anybody but the Vicar himself is empowered to convene such a meeting. Such resolutions as you saw fit to pass at that meeting are therefore completely null and void."

"Once again, if Major Icely had allowed me to finish what I was saying I could have saved him that interruption," said Jones equably. "It has never been suggested—except by Mr. Insight—that our meeting had any official status whatsoever.

No minutes were kept and no resolutions passed. All that transpired was an exchange of views and the drafting of the letter which, I notice with interest, Major Icely now dignifies by the name of 'document'. We never claimed to speak as the Standing Committee. We spoke purely as a body of friends gathered together to discuss and pronounce on a subject of vital interest to us all."

He sat down to a small chorus of 'hear, hears', though not to the enthusiasm I had anticipated. By now my head ached and my mouth was parched by anxiety. A craven desire to retreat for ever from all this unpleasantness swept over me but I knew I must see it through. I took a grip on myself and said: "I am afraid it must be clear to all present that the wardens and I have lost confidence in each other. I regret it deeply, and am prepared to do anything to restore the situation short of betraying what I believe to be right."

After this, several people got up to speak and I was more than a little touched by how many of them came down firmly on my side. But nothing of real value was achieved, the rift was as wide open as ever.

At the close of the meeting no one seemed eager to leave the hall. Little groups formed, free now to talk as hard as they liked. Icely had been buttonholed by Bresewell, whom I felt sure must be on my side, and I caught his eye and waved a farewell before slipping out quietly by the side door.

In the village there were footsteps behind me and Mrs. Charmian's voice called, "Vicar—just a minute!" I stopped and she caught up with me. "Vicar, you're not depressed, are you?"

"I don't know how to feel," I said as we continued walking. "It did seem to go better this time."

"Oh, it did, it did; Many of them had no idea that things had gone on so far behind the scenes. I'm sure it will be all right now."

"Come back to the vicarage with me," I said impulsively, "and have a chat with Margaret. It will cheer her up. The poor girl has to suffer all the antagonism stirred up by me."

Margaret was glad to see Mrs. Charmian and soon produced

tea and biscuits. She was anxious to know how things had gone but could see that I was tired with the strain of it all.

"What you need, Jim," she said, "is to relax in a good, hot bath. Go on. Mrs. Charmian will excuse you, and she can tell me everything." Wonderful Margaret, who always knew what was best for me. Beautiful Margaret, who was now looking a little paler and a little thinner because she always put my welfare before her own.

Lying in the steaming water, I began to feel more optimistic about things. It was awful that there should be quarrels in the last place where one would expect them, the church of God— but there were occasions when not to fight would be wrong. I'd have to get Icely's opinion on that. In the meantime I'd have to make the best of it until the whole nasty business came up again at the Annual General Meeting, still some months ahead. But perhaps that wouldn't be necessary. Maybe, by some miracle, we really would forget the past and be able to work happily together. Or perhaps, after to-night's affray, the wardens would resign. I scooped up the sponge and reached for the soap. That would be the real answer. If only the wardens would resign . . .

But there were no resignations from the wardens. Instead, the situation deteriorated. On the Sunday following the P.C.C., although both men were in church, neither appeared in the vestry. It was the same at the evening service and for the following two Sundays. Evidently they did not intend to see me unless forced to do so. This meant that no one found the lessons in the lectern Bible—a small matter, but one that did not go unnoticed by some of the members of the congregation.

As Vicar, I knew that I should be at one with my wardens planning happily for the work of God in St. Hilda's. Instead, two things were obvious. One. That the village were convinced that the three of us had had a flaming row and now hated the sight of each other. Two. That it was up to me to try and heal the breach, and at least suggest the three of us be seen together from time to time. In this way there would be the appearance of unity.

The nervous tension engendered by worrying over what I was to do was having its effect on my health so that, at times, I found it hard to keep still, was for ever springing up wondering if I should make new proposals, and had difficulty in concentrating.

There was nothing to do except try once more to have at least part of the matter out with the wardens and suggest we meet together in public lest the village really believe we had quarrelled.

"But we have quarrelled, haven't we, Vicar?" said Charrington-Hawes regretfully when, at last, I got hold of him. We were walking down the main street of the village and I tried to look as pleasant as I could so that passers-by who intended to gossip would say to their neighbours, 'Of course they're friends'.

"I don't want it to be a quarrel," I said. "I just want us to see each other, to meet more, and not to appear to be always avoiding each other."

"But if we haven't your confidence, what's the use? Ah, there's Jones. Let's get hold of him."

Jones looked as if he were going to try to escape but gave in. Charrington-Hawes, who appeared to be taking everything well in his stride, said, "Mr. Jones, the Vicar doesn't think we see enough of each other. How do you feel?"

"Any time the Vicar wants, I'll meet him," said Jones affably.

It wasn't as easy as all that. Deep in my heart I knew that things could never again be the same. I felt as a man must feel whose wife has left him; still loving her, he can't let her go though he knows nothing in the future can ever be the same. Searching my mind in the High Street, with people we all knew passing to and fro, I knew that for the sake of the congregation I had to appear to be at one with these men; but I also knew I would never be really happy until they were replaced. I had nothing against them, but I could no longer work with them.

As if knowing what I was thinking, Jones said, "We can't resign, you know, Vicar. We must hold office until the Annual Meeting."

"Oh! That is not so. It would be quite in order for you to resign. In fact, it would help a lot."

"It's real effect would be to suggest that in the dispute between us you were right, Vicar, and we were wrong," Charrington-Hawes pointed out.

"I don't think that that need arise," I said quietly. "I would undertake to correct any such impression. After all, the difference between us is not a straight one of right and wrong, but of what we individually believe to be right and wrong. Unhappily, it has now progressed beyond this stage, and for this I must acknowledge to be no less to blame than you. We have allowed the situation to degenerate into one of incompatibility, and I regret deeply that it should be so."

"Aye, that's true," Jones said, "but I still don't see why we should back down from our beliefs by resigning."

"Now, Mr. Jones, you are being guided solely by pride," I said. "That's unworthy of you."

"Well, aren't you, too?" he demanded defensively.

His question came as a considerable shock.

"I don't know," I said at last. "Perhaps I am, but remember this is my job. I like to believe it's even more—that it's my calling. I have so many more considerations to bear in mind than you—my wife, my family, my professional integrity. You're not asking that I should resign, are you?"

"That should hardly be necessary," Charrington-Hawes intervened hastily.

"Then what would you have me do?"

Neither replied, and we walked on in silence for some minutes. It was I who broke the silence.

"Look, gentlemen," I said, "the Annual General Meeting is still some way off. What will be its outcome I can only guess. But one thing is immediately apparent; in the interval the three of us must not only work more closely together, but must appear to work more closely together. However we may feel privately towards each other, for the sake of the church for which we all work we must conceal these signs of discord. Will you not at least agree to that?"

"I will," said Jones, readily enough.

"I, too," said Charrington-Hawes.

"Thank you, both of you," I said, and we shook hands all round.

St. Hilda's police station is really a cottage, its true purpose betrayed by one or two police notices and the blue lamp outside. The resident policeman, a homely man named Briggs, stood now with tunic unbuttoned behind a little counter, making notes as I spoke.

"Yes, sir," he said, speaking with a thick country burr, "I remember the excitement over Challump and how Mr. Bigwood squashed it. I think the best thing would be to have a plain-clothes man in the congregation in case his brother tries anything on."

"I'd be most grateful," I said.

"Be glad to do it, sir. Things are pretty quiet these days. That letter of yours certainly did a bit of good. Since it came out in the newspapers the kids seem to be scared to get up to their pranks because their parents come down on them like a ton of bricks. Now, then, let's get this detail down for the Challump affair . . ."

As he spoke, his pen ran dry and I handed mine across to him. There was a sort of buzzing in my ears and my hand trembled violently. He couldn't fail to notice.

"Are you feeling all right, sir?" he asked anxiously.

I tried to reply but no words came. Instead I seemed to hear his voice repeating the question from a great distance, like the echo in a vast cave—"Are you feeling all right, sir?" "Are you feeling all right, sir?" "Are you feeling all right, sir . . . ?"

The dead face of Mrs. Markesete swam before me. The deterioration had gone on and on, as I knew it must—the skin drying on her frame, the eyes receding deep into their sockets, the tired heart coming slowly to its final beat. Perhaps the worst of it was the agony on her husband's face as he forced himself again and again to the bedside to lay his hand on the sheet so that she should know he was there if she needed him. It made me wonder inconsequently if she could ever have loved him as much as he loved her.

When it was over, I'd urged him to take a holiday, to go abroad, to get away from it all. He'd been hesitant and I'd used the trite words "She would want you to do that."

The strain of the sickroom, the long struggle with the wardens —it was all having its effect. Sensitive to the feelings of others, I found significance in every word, every gesture. Every remark seemed to have an underlying implication. It wasn't the words themselves, I told myself, but what lay behind them. Who was for me? Who was against me?

So the struggle continued from day to day—now hopeful, now filled with despair; one moment determined to fight for what I believed in, the next prepared to throw in the towel; here being slighted and there receiving an unexpected word of encouragement. And all the time worrying about what effect all this was having on Margaret.

The Honeymoon Village, so earnestly desired and happily accepted, now assumed in my mind the character of a small jungle in which the forces of darkness prevailed. The church, which should have been the antidote to all the evil now seemed to be the place where it lurked and thrived.

David's definition of life floated back to me, spoken in his serio-comic style as we had laughed and drunk coffee together in our curate days. "It's like something you find beneath a large stone, Jim—creatures rushing here and there, hating the light, burrowing and delving. All you can do is slam the stone down and pretend it never happened or spring about the place jumping on them. Neither does any good, old boy. All perfectly scriptural, of course." He'd begun to quote: "The heart is deceitful above all things and desperately . . ."

"I do know a bit of the Bible, David," I'd said.

But nothing would quell him. "Of course you do. That is what we Anglos and you Evangelicals have in common. I forgot."

"What can one do about it all?" I'd asked.

"The Bible?"

"The stone."

"Only what Christ did. Live in the light."

Again the voice echoed in the cavern—"In the light." "In the light." "In the light..."

Suddenly the darkness lifted and a man was doing something to my back collar stud. What on earth had happened? I appeared to be sitting on a chair and leaning forward. Briggs was standing beside me and I thought how round and smooth and shining the toes of his boots were.

"I can't think what happened..." I began.

"You fainted, sir."

"Did I? I—I've never fainted before."

He lifted the flap of the counter and helped me through into his back parlour, where his wife was pouring tea. She must have been told. They didn't fuss around me or make me feel that anything untoward had occurred, talking politely instead about superficial things. But the idea of fainting was so new to me that I couldn't leave it alone. I wanted to know how long I'd been out and whether they'd sent for the doctor or anything like that.

"No, Vicar," said Mrs. Briggs, refilling my cup. "I don't think it was anything much. I expect you've been working too hard. Yours is a busy life."

After a while, I thanked them and said that I must be on my way.

"Briggs will go with you," said his wife.

"No—er—no, thanks. I feel fine now." If the village saw the policeman with me there'd be a new crop of rumours. I stood up, relieved to find that I was steady on my feet. "I wonder if I could ask a favour of you both?"

"Certainly, sir," said Briggs.

"If you should meet my wife, please don't say anything to her about this. You see, she hasn't been too well herself recently and it would only worry her."

"That'll be all right, sir. We won't say a word," said Mrs. Briggs. "Not a word. D'you hear that, Briggs? You are not to say anything to the vicar's wife; not to anyone, for that matter. You know how rumours get around."

More cheerful now, I walked home. The children were chasing

each other across the lawn, falling down and picking themselves
up again, shrieking and laughing. They were too immersed to
notice my arrival, and I went into the house to find Margaret.
She was not in the kitchen, as I'd expected she might be, but
in the study with a pile of women's magazines. Near at hand
were the tea things. She looked relaxed and comfortable, glancing
up and smiling as I came in.

"Hullo, darling," she said. "How's things?"

I closed the door and stood with my back to it. And such is the
strangeness of human behaviour, I now said exactly what I'd
been determined not to say.

"Margaret...I fainted this afternoon...at the police
station..."

Then I burst into tears.

Unhitching his stethoscope from his ears, the doctor looked at
me and smiled. "Nothing organically wrong," he said, "but I'd
like you to stay in bed for the next week. Can you do that?"

"Yes," said Margaret before I could open my mouth.

"What's wrong, then, doctor?" I wanted to know.

"Well, I'd say you've been overdoing it one way or the other.
What you need is complete rest." He looked at me quizzically
and I knew that he must be well acquainted with the facts. He
couldn't cover a village like this and not know. As a Roman
Catholic, however, he was aloof from the internecine strife in
which I was engaged.

The next few days consisted mainly of sleep—uneasy, turbulent
sleep filled with weird dreams in which Charrington-Hawes and
Jones figured prominently. Once, they both clambered into the
wardrobe and sat hunched together amongst Margaret's dresses
discussing me.

During waking hours there was a continuing cloud across my
brain. When Margaret said anything, I had to repeat the sen-
tence to myself before the sense of it penetrated. Concentration
was difficult and I could only read a page or two of a book
before throwing it to the end of the bed. Susan and Robert were
distant but constant "noises off"—and when they were allowed

into the bedroom, although my heart leapt to see them side by side bringing me things they'd picked in the garden, it wasn't long before I wished them gone.

While my body rested, my mind whirled busily on. And now I thought of Margaret having to cope with everything herself— the house, the children, the garden, the parish. She'll soon be ill again too, I thought and, thinking it, the tears coursed silently down my cheeks; tears of misery and self-pity. What is to become of us all, I wondered desperately. What should I have done to avert this trouble? Should I have sunk my own beliefs for the good of the Church and the community as a whole? After all, I was not opposed to scamps and vagabonds. I had every reason to believe that the men and women of my Standing Committee were no less honest in their opinions than I was in mine. They could be right and I wrong. After all, there were some twenty of them and only one of me. But if that had been the case, would I have felt so strenuously that I was right, and I had never felt more so in all my life? Usually in an argument I see the other man's point of view so clearly that I have difficulty in doing justice to my own. But in this instance there was no shadow of doubt as to my proper course of action and something within me told me I must at all costs hold on.

Propped up in bed, I tried to enjoy breakfast, spreading butter on toast and reflecting that in so many ways a person's Christian belief often appeared to have little to do with his behaviour. People seemed to be either nice or not nice, and their profession of faith affected the issue very little. Such thoughts took me back to David's stone, and suddenly I pushed the breakfast tray from me in revulsion, my mouth full of insects.

After a few days, however, Margaret unexpectedly lifted the ban on visitors by throwing open the bedroom door and saying, "Jim, there's someone to see you."

Major Icely, in a smart clerical-grey suit, strolled into the room. "Hullo, there, old boy!" he exclaimed. "Greetings from the parish." He lowered himself carefully into the small bedside chair. "There are all sorts of rumours around concerning the state of your health. According to one woman you're not even

here. She saw the ambulance carry you off with her own eyes."
He laughed, and so did I. It seemed strange to be laughing again
and I suddenly felt very much better.

"Are you what the doctor ordered?" I asked. "Because if so,
it works."

"That's good. I'm Margaret's prescription, actually. Supposed
to buck you up and all that." He was in excellent form and there
was an air of suppressed excitement about him. It was obvious
that something had happened, something about which he was
very pleased. My immediate thought was that it was something
to do with the church, but as he went on talking I realised
that it couldn't be. For though we talked at length about the
church, the excitement stayed with him, remaining outside our
conversation. Whatever it is, I thought, he'll tell me when he
wants to.

Strangely enough, I now found it easy to talk about the
situation in the church quite rationally and calmly.

"I'd like to get something settled about the Annual Meeting,"
I said. "You know—make up my mind what I intend to do."

"No need to worry about it now. There's still plenty of time."

"I know—but I'd feel easier if I could get it settled in my
mind."

"All right," he said, as though recognising my return to
normalcy, "let's sort it out. What are we after? You want to put
into effect the original intention of the Canon of 1603 and elect
two wardens of whom both you and the meeting approve. Is
that it?"

"Yes. Two new men."

"Right."

"And I want you to be one of them," I said firmly.

"Oh! Oh, you do, do you? Well, well! Ha! Well, I've never
been a warden in my life, but I'd do my very best . . . That's that,
then. What about the other man?"

"That's what's been worrying me. Unless we get a man the
meeting approve, we're sunk; because they'll put in Charrington-
Hawes or Jones."

"I see. Have you anyone else in mind?"

"Not really. Mr. Bresewell?" I suggested dubiously.

"Too religious!"

We laughed at the paradox and I tried again. "Sir Henry Triscombe, then?"

"Too aloof. Don't you think so?"

"Yes," I agreed. "I hardly know him, or anything about him, but..."

"The people wouldn't vote for him. It's got to be someone they'll vote for. Otherwise, however good he may be, it's useless."

"What about Bill Tomlinson? He's been coming along so well recently."

"He'd be grand," said Icely, "but they'd never accept him. You've got to be in the church for years and years if people are going to have you as a warden."

"It's difficult, isn't it?"

"It is, indeed. I give up. How about you? You going to have another shot?"

"Yes," I said, "I am. What about Mrs. Pankhurst?"

"*Norah?*" Icely practically shouted. "Norah! Great Scott! That would put the cat among the pigeons... Oh, my sainted aunt! Norah and me! Suppose we were elected. Can you imagine what the village would make of that? Particularly since——" He threw back his head, slapping his knees and roaring with laughter.

"Particularly since what?" I asked.

"Oh, my goodness!" he hooted. "Oh, my jolly old word!"

Margaret, coming in with coffee on a tray, looked at Icely approvingly. "You're doing him good," she said happily.

"*Me* doing *him* good?" Icely gurgled, wiping tears of laughter from his cheeks with his fist. "I like that! It's him doing me good. You'll never guess who he's just suggested as a warden. Oh, my purple whiskers! Norah, Margaret. Can you credit that? Norah Pankhurst."

"You've been talking shop," said Margaret accusingly, "and the doctor said he was to get his mind off church matters. I warned you."

"I know—but he wanted to, and it hasn't done him any harm. Has it, Jim?"

"You can have a woman warden," I said. "Dorothy Sayers was one."

"She's downstairs," Margaret announced.

"Never!" I gasped. "She can't be, she's . . ."

"Norah Pankhurst, I mean. She called to ask how you are. She'd like to come up just for a minute." Margaret's eyes twinkled. "Would you mind, Major?"

Icely pulled a face. "Certainly not. She'll be our Huldah. We shall consult the oracle."

Margaret departed and within minutes we heard feet ascending the stairs.

Mrs. Pankhurst came cautiously round the door and Icely stood up.

"Oh!" The Pankhurst cheeks reddened. "I hope I'm not disturbing you. It was just that——" She came forward and put a small tin of biscuits on the eiderdown as if the gift were of no consequence. The humility of her action touched me deeply and, I believe, must have had some effect on Icely.

"Norah," he said gently, "Norah, my dear, come and sit down in this chair—here. We have something for you to do. A little problem we'd like you to solve. You've lived here all your life. You know the parish and the church inside out. We're planning for the Annual General Meeting and Jim wants me to be one of the wardens. Problem—who is the other to be? It must be someone who is acceptable to the people—or they won't vote for him —and to the vicar, who has to work with him. We've thought and thought without getting anywhere. Now—who? Take your time. There's no hurry; but it has to be the right person."

She sat thinking, absently accepting the cup of coffee he gave her, and time seemed to stand still while she gave the matter her consideration. She was not a woman to give a decision lightly and we both had great faith in her judgment of character. Watching them both, I couldn't help thinking how well suited they were to each other. If only . . . But it was no time to think of such things and I began to pray, instead, that she would find the right answer.

"I think I've got it," she said suddenly.

"Yes?" prompted Icely.

"He's well known—a splendid man. The only problem is whether he will agree to have his name put forward."

"Who, Norah—who is it?"

She made us wait for the answer, confident in her choice. Then she said, "Mr. Thomas."

There was silence while we thought about it. Thomas—principal of the College. Thomas—member of the P.C.C. Thomas—intellectual, understanding, disciplined. Of course. Why hadn't I thought of him myself?

"She's right, you know," said Icely.

"Yes," I agreed, "and when I'm up and about I'll sound him."

My head was beginning to ache and they both seemed to sense that the visit had lasted long enough. Before they left, Icely crossed to the bed and patted the sheets. "Hurry up and get well, Jim. You and Margaret must come to one of my little dinners—rather a special one. I'm not going to have it unless you are both there."

Later, when Margaret was rearranging my pillows, I said, "Something has happened to the major. I don't know what it is, but he seems different somehow."

"What would you like for your dinner?" was Margaret's reply. But I knew she had been putting her mind back to the visit to see if I was right for she added, "You and your intuitions!"

★ 12 ★

Mrs. Charmian came to sit in with Robert and Susan on the night of Icely's dinner party. They loved her coming and could hardly wait for us to be on our way. Laughing, we allowed ourselves to be pushed from the front door.

"Don't hurry back," Mrs. Charmian called. "It doesn't matter how late you are. Just have a good time."

Chaffing each other about how unnecessary we were to our family, Margaret and I set off on our walk to The Nook.

Since I had recovered from my breakdown, both people and the church had lost some of their terror for me. Just the same, a few of the old fears were not far from the surface. Prior to the days of the meeting my policy had been to greet every man as a friend, to love and help and serve and minister. Now it was as if the platform of life had been kicked from under me. The trouble lay in the fact that both Charrington-Hawes and Jones were men of sterling worth; I had no difficulty in acknowledging this and yet, after what had happened, I knew I was temperamentally—one might almost say pathologically—incapable of working in harmony with them. It worried me that this should be so, and I suffered anxious moments of heart-searching that in the gulf that had come between us I and not they might be the one at fault.

Some such thought were still running through my mind, as we reached Icely's house. This was not the first of his dinner parties we had attended. Usually they were small, cosy affairs—never more than three or four guests, often just Margaret and me. On this occasion, though, there was a more festive air and a larger gathering. We had expected to see Mrs. Pankhurst and the doctor, but were surprised and pleased to find Mrs. Atwell, the rural dean and Irene among those present. There were also two or three other young people we had never seen before. Muted music provided a background to conversation and everything seemed light and joyful.

"It's like a celebration," whispered Margaret as the rural dean, supported by a stick and his daughter's arm, made his way over to us.

"I hear you've been ill, Insight," he said. "Hope things are better now—in the parish, too."

"Thank you, sir, I am much better. I wish I could say as much of the climate in the parish."

"No improvement, eh?"

"Well, a little perhaps in that I have got two excellent men who are prepared to act as wardens given the opportunity. The trouble is my present wardens show no signs of resigning. I really believe they look on their work as wardens in almost the vocational light that I regard mine as a priest."

"When you've been at it as long as I have, Insight, you'll find people think they have every right to tell the church what to do. I'm sure a number of your P.C.C. believe they are your employers and that the bishop is some benign adviser to whom they can send petitions if things don't turn out the way they expect."

Irene laughed. "Shop, Daddy!" Then she turned to us. "I'm so glad you're both here to-night, because——"

"Irene," said Icely, looming up, "Rural Dean—a thousand apologies, but may I carry the vicar and his missus away for a moment? Something rather important. Won't take long."

He propelled us from the room, stopping in the hall outside what he called his den.

"There, now! We can hear ourselves talk."

"There's something afoot, as they say," said Margaret. "I'm sure of it."

Icely laughed. "Good girl. There are a number of things afoot, as they say. It's a night of surprises. There's one in there——" he indicated his den, "but there's another one I have to spring on you first. Can you both stand a shock?"

"I can if he can," said Margaret.

"Right. You may have wondered about this celebration dinner." He paused. "I'm engaged to be married."

"*What!*" we chorused.

"It's not possible!" said Margaret.

"Well, thank you for that flattering comment," chuckled Icely, "but it is possible. In fact, I *am*."

"But who is it?" urged Margaret. "Who?"

"Can't you guess?"

We looked at each other. Margaret had become a different person—alert, alive. One name occurred to us simultaneously. "Norah!"

Icely smiled and kept us waiting.

"It is!" said Margaret, excited.

"I'm sorry, but it could never have been her. Jim knows that. I've told her about it, though, and she's delighted for me."

Margaret was puzzled. "But it can't be anyone else here. They're all married."

"All except one."

I knew then, but it was so unexpected I couldn't put it into words. "Not Irene?"

He nodded. "Irene. It's fantastic, I know; it's ridiculous and it's unbelievable. I'm old, old, old, and she's just a girl. I've gone mad, and so has she. We love each other. We're going to be married. It's as simple and as complicated as that. We're going to make the announcement at dinner, but I had to let you know before that. Couldn't have you both collapsing into the pheasant."

"It's wonderful," said Margaret, leaning forward and kissing him lightly on the cheek. "Congratulations, and bless you. But I didn't even know that you and Irene knew each other."

"Well, it's rather odd, really. I'd seen her in the village and couldn't help noticing her, of course. But wherever I went I seemed to run into her—almost as though I was following her about. A bit embarrassing, really. She didn't seem to mind. Said she got on better with older men anyway. And there it was. It happened so often that, before I knew where I was, I was in love with her. Like a miracle. As though Fate had planned it."

Fate, I thought, with red hair.

"Congratulations," I said. "And you're not too old. You're young, and she's lucky. You're both lucky. She's a wonderful girl. All I ask is that you'll let me marry you when the time comes."

"Thank you both," he replied. "And so to surprise number two." He opened the door of his den and stood aside for us to enter.

In the den a large man in a cassock stood munching a savoury and licking his fingers.

"*David!*" I gasped. "What on earth are *you* doing here?"

"Let me kiss Margaret first, then I'll tell you." He was enjoying the situation, playing it blandly in contrast to our astonishment.

"I don't want to be kissed," said Margaret. "Not with beard *and* sardine. Just tell us how you come to be here. As briefly as possible."

"Well," David replied, reaching for another savoury, "it's all quite simply explained. It seems that you mentioned my name to the Major more than once in past conversations as the Brain of Britain in the settling of all parochial contretemps. It is a small reputation I have in which, with great modesty, I heartily concur. So what more natural than that the gallant Major should invite me to be his guest at this delightful party, and at the same time untangle the coil in which you now find yourself."

I was touched. "You came all this way simply——" I began.

"Simply to enjoy the party. Unfortunately, Amanda couldn't come—but there's an absolutely ravishing redhead in the other room . . ." He looked with mock innocence at Icely.

"Yes," I said hastily. "Now, what do you already know?"

"Only that she seems to be quite perfect and——Oh, you mean about *your* how-d'you-do. Everything, I think. The major has been most concise. But before I pronounce judgment, I'd like to get one or two things quite straight." He caressed his beard, obviously enjoying every minute of his Solomon role. "The Annual General Meeting . . . If you can't agree on the choice of wardens, then you will choose yours and they will have to choose theirs—correct?"

"Yes."

"Would you choose Charrington-Hawes?"

"No, of course not—that's the whole point."

"Does he know that?"

"I should imagine it must be self-evident. We just can't work together, and that's all there is to it."

"If you don't ask him to be your warden again before the Meeting, what then? Do you think he will resign?"

"No, I don't. But I wish he would. It would certainly help matters."

"Yes ... well, more of that later. Let's assume that he does resign. That leaves Jones. What will you do if he's re-elected?"

"I shall object," I said. "Don't get me wrong. I'm sure he's a good man, I know he's a kind one, but I can't work with him. Not any more. I can't work with anyone unless there's harmony between us, and whatever harmony we might have once shared was forfeited when he signed that document."

"Yes, yes, I see that. But suppose there is a deadlock. Suppose the meeting wants him and you don't. What then?"

"Well, that's it. By law, if we can't agree they can choose any man they like and I can choose anyone I like."

"Right." He pondered for a moment, then he turned to Icely. "Major, I am about to hatch a plot. Jim is awfully sensitive about such things and is liable to quail. Why don't you take Margaret back to the music, gaiety and laughter? Then Jim will be saved the embarrassment of having the vapours in front of an audience. We'll join you in a minute or two. It's the party I really came for, remember."

When they had gone, David helped himself to another savoury and consumed it carefully before speaking.

"First of all," he said, "you should know I've been to see Uncle Charrington-Hawes. I went straight there after my arrival here. We had a long talk together. He's a good chap, you know, Jim. A bit pompous, some might think, but as straight as a string. He earnestly believes that what he did was right and for the good of the community. I reversed the relationship between us and talked to him like a Dutch uncle. What is more, he listened. I told him that the rights and wrongs of this case no longer mattered; they are too trivial to be worth a light, anyway.

What matters now, I said, was the unity of St. Hilda's; compared with this all other considerations paled to insignificance. And Heaven alone knows that's true, Jim!"

"Yes," I agreed, unhappily aware I was not entirely blameless in this.

"Then I hit the old fellow a bit below the belt. I asked him if he was going to allow his own bigotry to stand in the way of the healing of past wounds. That hurt him because what is bigotry to one man is right-minded determination to another. Well, I'm not saying he hasn't got his faults, but pettiness isn't one of them. Making it quite clear that he did not retract one thing he had said or done, he eventually went on to say that if his resignation would clear the air of tension and mistrust, you should have it forthwith. So there you are, Jim."

"It's generous of him."

"Damn generous. Moreover, believing that least said soonest mended, he proposes to give as his reason for resigning a trip round the world, or something equally inoffensive. The old boy's rolling in dough, so he'll probably do just that."

"David, I just don't know what to say."

"Say nothing. Well, that would seem to dispose of one uncle. Now what about this other beezer—Jones. What are we going to do about him?"

"You tell me," I replied, incapable of further thought.

A broad smile spread over the flaming beard. "I think we shall have to remove him. As painlessly as possible."

Having to remove someone, even metaphorically, was not pleasant. I tried to think of it as a political assassination but that didn't help. Only the thought that it was for the good of the church brought me any comfort. I had to look upon it as a sort of Crusade. That the victim had to be Jones was regrettable, for I was unable to forget his former kindnesses. Nevertheless, there was no alternative. He was the only obstacle to the unity I sought.

During the intervening months between the night of Icely's party and the night of the Annual General Meeting David's prophecy had come true. Charrington-Hawes had resigned. In a formal letter of resignation he had explained that his reason for doing so was solely that he intended making a long-delayed world tour. Since there was no knowing how long he would be away, he felt that it would be best for him to resign before the Annual General Meeting, thus giving me an opportunity to find someone to replace him. I had, of course, accepted his resignation and called to see him and his wife before their departure. Charrington-Hawes had intimated that Mr. Jones might be the best person to take his place, leaving another people's warden to be found.

That had been a week ago. Now it was the night of the Annual General Meeting and Mr. Jones was due to be removed. With a file of papers beneath my arm, and feeling wobbly at the knees, I kissed Margaret good-bye.

"Lots of luck, darling," she said. "It will soon be over." She meant the meeting, of course, for she knew nothing of the proposed removal. "Try to think of all those in the hall who will be on your side."

There were many people in the building when I arrived and I heard someone say in surprise that it was the best attended meeting in the history of St. Hilda's. The chairs were set in rows facing the platform, on which a table was framed by draped curtains. It reminded me of a scaffold.

Tea was handed round and we made desultory conversation. In any other circumstances I would have found it all very pleasant. The whole tone of the meeting would normally have been spiritual and friendly, for Mr. Bigwood, during his incumbency, had succeeded in removing any starchy business-meeting atmosphere and replacing it with warm friendliness. Perhaps to others it still seemed that way, but I was filled with the knowledge of what lay ahead.

At last it was time to get down to business and I sought out Icely. "This is it!" I murmured. "Shall we start?"

He nodded. "Don't lose your nerve, now," he said as we walked side by side to the platform. Even he had no idea of what I intended to do, though. To me it seemed a dreadful thing, an utterly un-Christian thing that would be bound to shock and amaze almost everyone present. But if it had to be done, I would do it.

Jones joined us and we acknowledged each other briefly. He took a place on the platform to my left, with Icely, as secretary, just beyond him. On my right was Sir Henry, who would be giving his financial report.

We opened with prayer and this was followed by the report of the last Annual General Meeting. While it was being read the tension in the hall could be felt. Everyone knew something of what had been going on, but most of them had been fed on rumours and conjectures. My stomach seemed to be turning to water and I began to pray inwardly: "O God, do help me. I want only to try and serve Thee with others in this parish and church. I love this place and, though You may not think it, I do try to love people. It's just that I'm lost with people who don't like me. I curl up and know not how to treat them. Lord, help me to deliver the statement I have ready and, if I have to take the extreme step and it seems wrong in Thy sight, please forgive me. I will do it only if it seems the only way to further Thy work in this church."

Opening my eyes, I saw Mrs. Pankhurst in the second row. Her face was set in the lines of goodness and truth. Behind her was Mrs. Charmian. The immediate sight of two whom I knew to be friends encouraged me. Without standing up I asked for approval to sign the minutes just read, then scrawled my name.

Rising, I slipped sheets of paper from my file, comforting myself with the thought that unless it became absolutely necessary there would be no removal. Perhaps Jones would decline to stand for election, even at the last minute, and all would be well.

"Ladies and gentlemen," I began, "may I welcome you all to our Annual General Meeting. It's nice to see so many of you here. As you know, we are required by law to begin with the vestry meeting at which the election of the wardens takes place..."

The typescript, long prepared, took us slowly and carefully back to the ancient Canon, explaining how it was meant to be applied.

"... although in many parishes a vicar's warden and a people's warden are elected—the vicar nominating his man and the people theirs—this is not the intention of the law. What the Canon strives to demonstrate is that, above all, the church needs unity..."

Although read very slowly and with long pauses, I knew that it wasn't easy to understand. Only because I'd lived and slept with it for months on end did I know it inside out. When I'd read it to Margaret she'd laughed and said, "They'll be so confused at the end of that that they'll vote whichever way you want them to." But this I knew they would not do. Misunderstanding would most likely drive them back to the old way simply because it was the way they knew. Nevertheless, I could find no method of making the statement any simpler.

"We want to try first of all," I said, "to elect two men whom you want as wardens and of whom I approve. If we can do that, there will be unity. If not, then I must choose a man to be my warden and you must choose one to be yours."

Now came the tricky bit. Now it was time for the knife to be unsheathed in readiness. Pray God it would not have to be used. If the meeting spoke with one voice, could not this be the leading of God? For the rest, it was sheer politics. Icely would be proposed as one of the wardens and Thomas as the other, and I would accept them both—and if the meeting approved them we would have unity in the church. That was the plan. The one point I'd needed guidance on had been whether or not Jones should be warned of our intentions. I had, of course, told him unofficially some months earlier that I would welcome a change, so it couldn't come as a complete surprise to him. Nevertheless, it seemed to me that I owed it to him to tell him of our present plans. It would also give him the chance to resign if he wished, though I did not think this was likely. But Margaret, Icely and Mrs. Pankhurst, although consulted separately and independently, had been unanimous. It would be best, each of them advised, for me to keep my own counsel. Just the same, right up to the moment of mounting the platform there had been endless pressure on my conscience to have a word with Jones. It was too late now, and if it became necessary, David's plot to remove him would have to be put into effect.

"Normally," I said, "we would elect together the two men who have been wardens over the past year—Mr. Charrington-Hawes and Mr. Jones. But two things prevent this. One is that Mr. Charrington-Hawes has resigned, and the other is that I, personally, would like a change of wardens. Many of you will have already heard of differences that have arisen between myself and the wardens..." How easy it seemed to talk of these unpleasant things! The words were coming out like any other words. It was what went on inside that wasn't so easy. "If any of you would like me to explain it in detail, I shall be glad to do so now or at some other time."

There wasn't much more to be said. It was nearly over: a word about the great need to work together as a congregation; a remark of the rural dean's to the effect that none should expect a vicar to be impartial concerning the choice of his own wardens; and finally a plea that we should now set to work for the glory of God. You could have heard a pin drop when I'd finished.

Then Mrs. Pankhurst stood up and said she would like to propose Major Icely as one of the wardens. Rather to my surprise, Bresewell leapt up and seconded this. There were murmurs of approval from the body of the hall. All was going well. Oh, good, good! "Please God," I prayed, "let us get this dreadful business over and start building again." It was now that I expected Bill Tomlinson to get up and propose Thomas. I saw him moving in his chair, but before he could get to his feet someone else had risen. It was Mr. Saigon.

"I would like to propose Mr. Jones," he said. "He's been a warden for a number of years and I think he ought to be reelected."

Immediately there were cries from one or two others who agreed with the sentiment and wished to second the proposal. And then Tomlinson was speaking, proposing Mr. Thomas, and someone else was jumping up, not to second Thomas but to announce yet another name.

Oh, no! I thought. This was even more chaotic than I'd ever imagined. But it was essential that I shouldn't lose control. "Just a moment, just a moment!" I called. "There seem to be a number of nominations. We must find out first if those proposed wish to stand for election." I turned to the major, although I knew what his answer would be.

"Yes," he said, "I'm perfectly happy about it."

Turning to Mr. Jones I asked him how he felt about it, praying that he would refuse, that he would save me from striking the blow.

He stood up. "Yes," he said, "I'm quite happy to continue serving."

My heart sank and I steeled myself to kill. "I see," I said. For a moment I wavered and then I went on, clearly and loudly, "But Mr. Jones, I have made it abundantly clear that I would like to have *two* new wardens." The final thrust. "I yield to no one in appreciation of what you have done in the past, but I think the time has now come for a change."

There was a sort of communal gasp from the audience, but Mr. Jones remained impregnable. He refused to be killed. Looking at me coolly, he said, "If the *people* want me as their warden, however, I shall still be happy to serve." Then he sat down, and I wondered how I could have been so wrong about him. I'd seen him, through all this, as Charrington-Hawes' stooge. At one time I'd even thought that with Charrington-Hawes' resignation he might come to me and apologise for his part in the affair. He'd always kept so much in the background. But now he was on his own he was quite undaunted.

It transpired that there were two other nominees, neither of them particularly well known to me, and I announced to the meeting that we would have to vote.

Pieces of paper were shot down the ranks, and pens and pencils were produced. Meanwhile the Canon of 1603 danced a jig in my head. Were we going to achieve unity in this way? If the voting went to Jones then I'd have to object again, and go on objecting until the meeting and I were forced to choose our own men. Emboldened by desperation, I stood up again.

"Ladies and gentlemen," I said, "you are about to tell me the names of the men you wish to be our wardens. Perhaps it is only fair that I should let you know the names of the two men with whom I would be happy to work in the year ahead." I had everyone's attention. "They are Major Icely and Mr. Thomas."

I sat down and waited for the voting slips to be collected and counted. At least everyone knew where everyone else stood. If the result was unacceptable . . .

One of the sidesmen was coming down the hall with a piece of paper. It could only be the result, and my stomach turned over. Why was he walking so slowly? How much longer could I stand the suspense?

The slip of paper was pushed on to the table in front of me and a single glance told me what I wanted to know. Major Icely's name came first . . . then Mr. Thomas . . . then Jones . . . I felt faint with relief. It hardly seemed possible that the long months of bickering, worrying and plotting were finally done with. I turned to flash a smile to Icely, but tears of joy were pricking my eyelids.

Announcing the result, I thanked everyone for their help and suggested that we now proceed to the Annual General Meeting proper. Before this, however, Jones stood up and made a short speech thanking everyone for their past support.

"I would like to say here and now," he said, "that I have never been prompted by personal animosity towards the vicar and if there's ever any way in which I can help the church I trust he will not hesitate to call on me."

So, like Charrington-Hawes, he was generous in defeat. I thanked him warmly and sincerely, my mind flashing back to his many kindnesses, and the friendliness he'd always shown the children, who adored him. I even half-regretted now that I hadn't allowed him to be re-elected. It might have worked after all. But I knew my conscience would continue to tell me things like that for quite some time. For I had personally removed Jones —just as David had advised.

"If all else fails," David had said earlier that night in Icely's den, "you must get up and denounce him publicly, tell the meeting quite definitely that you will not have him as a warden. You are the vicar, their spiritual leader. In the face of such a statement, the majority of them would not dare vote for Jones. It'll shock 'em—but if they're Christian enough to attend the meeting they'll recognise your authority *and* respect it. And poor old Jones will be down among the dead men . . .."

Nevertheless, I would read no burial service for Jones. I would take him at his word and, if he could help in some way, I would call on him. In that way, perhaps, I would be able to resurrect him. Because deep in my heart I knew I had done the right thing. Confident in the support of Icely and Thomas, I knew the true work of the church could be continued without hindrance.

It was a jubilant supper we had that night at the vicarage—Icely, Thomas and Mrs. Pankhurst having accompanied me to break the glad news to Margaret. There'd only been coffee and sandwiches to start with, but then Mrs. Charmian had put in an appearance and before long there were appetising plates of bacon, fried bread and eggs. The meeting was described in full, all of us talking at once to give our own impressions, with Mrs. Charmian breaking in to urge us to eat the food while it was hot. From there we went on to exchange ideas concerning the future of our church, which prompted Mrs. Pankhurst to call out good-naturedly to me, "And you're the man who was never going to discuss church matters!" There seemed so much to say that it looked as though we'd go on talking all night. In fact, it was two o'clock in the morning when our visitors departed, still in the highest of spirits. And at last Margaret and I were alone.

"I'm too excited to sleep," I said, "I could walk for miles, or talk for hours—or something."

"I know," she replied, coming close and giving me a kiss. "You're really happy now, aren't you?"

"Yes, I am—I am. Icely and Thomas are fine men. I'm positive now that the church will flourish. There's so much to be done, and they will help me to do it. We'll work so hard. The church will have to be re-decorated——"

"In time for the major's wedding, I hope."

"My goodness, I'd almost forgotten that! That's something to look forward to, isn't it? Oh, Margaret! Isn't life wonderful?"

"Yes, Jim—it is."

"Not that I expect everything to be happy-ever-after like a fairy tale. There are bound to be little upsets every now and then, things going wrong, problems cropping up. But the important thing is that now I feel I can face them. With Icely and Thomas I could face anything. And the great thing is that we can begin to build again . . ."

We stood in silence for a moment, thinking our own thoughts but sharing the same peaceful happiness.

Then Margaret took my hand. "Let's go and take a look at the children, shall we?" she said shortly. And hand in hand we tiptoed up the stairs.